WEATH THE STORMS

Living with and Understanding Epilepsy

JON SADLER

http://www.jonsadlerbooks.com

Scripture taken from the New King James Version ®. Copyright © 1982 by Thomas Nelson. Used by permission. All rights reserved.

For more information contact :

Brimingstone Press
5301 Alpha Rd, Suite 80 #200
Dallas, TX 75254
http://www.brimingstone.press

Book and Cover design by *Brimingstone Writer Services*

Edition : April 20, 2020

ISBN: 978-0-578-23285-0

Hope we have as an anchor of the soul.

—Hebrews 6:19 New King James Version
and the State Seal of Rhode Island

The tiniest sense of hope is the anchor that can overcome negative thoughts.

Contents

Introduction

It was the spring of 1963, I was four-years-old, and had the flu with a high fever. The seizure started in my sleep and lasted many hours. Treatment at the time was not nearly as extensive as today, however the impact to the family was as traumatic. My parents' generation grew up with an understanding that people diagnosed with epilepsy were to be treated similarly to someone with an infectious disease. In many states there were laws prohibiting people with epilepsy to be married to prevent it from spreading.

When I was in college, my father told me never to tell anyone about my epilepsy. He knew there would be times when people would label me, and I would be discriminated against simply because my brain would shut down on occasion. He was right in many ways; I would learn firsthand about the stigmas associated with having seizures. My fear was fed more by the outcome of a seizure than having one. Prayer became my outlet to maintain control of my emotions.

My seizures were managed for many years through medication. When a breakthrough seizure occurred, there seemed to be a new medication available, and the seizures were under control for a few more years. I was able to have a family and work as an engineer, and eventually became a project manager. My level of responsibility and the projects I was involved with were unique and important to the military.

Every time I would accomplish something important, either through work or family, there would be the setback of a seizure. Eventually, my seizures dominated my life; they reached the stage of being intractable, another term for untreatable. I went from a seizure every few years to several per week. Surgery, involving the removal of a section of my brain—the control center of my engineering skills—was the only option left.

I kept asking God, *why*? The answer to that question rarely comes immediately. For me this required waiting thirty-five years—the time it would take to have enough experience to help other people with epilepsy. The answer came through a phone call from a colleague whose child had intractable seizures; he and his family had lost all hope. Everything I had experienced now had meaning—a new beginning.

I was instilled with Hope early while struggling with understanding my seizures; now it was time share it with others. I became a mentor in the Epilepsy Foundation, helping people diagnosed with epilepsy and their families. Then, after having brain surgery, my counselor challenged me to go back to school to obtain a master's degree in Pastoral Counseling. This seemed impossible, because my memory was damaged and word recall poor.

Through my studies, I learned more about the brain and found many other situations people like myself faced—being broken, hopeless, and filled with anxiety and despair. My work as an intern focused on people dealing with addictions and others with brain injury and seizures.

My work also brought me in contact with the caregivers, mostly the family members who lived with the unknowns of seizures and struggled with relationships with whom they provided care. Being a caregiver for a person you love and who suffers from a seizure disorder is troubling and strenuous, both physically and mentally. I became the caregiver of a friend, who a few years ago, started having complex seizures. Living with and seeing many people having seizures should have made this easier. It didn't, because being the first responder is much different when it's the same person you care for have prolonged seizures several times a month.

My original book, *Sailing through the Storms of Seizures*, needed updating. The purpose of this one is the same—to help those who are struggling with or know someone who is dealing with epilepsy, brain injury, addiction, or some other disease or accident. The foundation I share about survival and recovery is based on three fundamentals: *perseverance, faith, and hope*.

This book is about how I have lived with epilepsy for over fifty years. The people and events in this book are real. There were many people who I have had contact with who helped me live with my fears or provided medical treatment. I cannot remember all the names, and maybe that is a good thing because I want to make sure their privacy is maintained. For those I do remember, their names have been changed; the exception is with family and those whose full names are presented.

The people referenced in my clinical work may consist of a summary of a group of people I worked or associated with.

The institutions and agencies mentioned truly exist, and the contact information is provided at the end to the book. Further information concerning education, treatment, and chat groups are available through these agencies. Some very good chat groups and other resources may be found on Facebook.

Section 1
Understanding Epilepsy

Chapter 1
The Brain and Seizures

Epilepsy is not a punishment on a person or their family for something they have done. It is a condition of the brain requiring respect, knowledge, and care. Control comes through the ability to live without the fear of rejection

Our brain is the most fascinating component of our bodies. It is the center of our nervous system, consisting of over a trillion neurons, and communicates with electrical impulses to all the parts of our body. It then activates and monitors body, including what we feel, taste, smell, see, and hear. It is the center of our emotions, how we feel about ourselves, our likes and dislikes, and responds accordingly. It is the master control center.

We hear many sounds around us and the brain deciphers which one to focus on. Vision is based on the light contacting our eyes and the brain's ability to send signals to the pupils to adjust the brightness, then processes the objects and colors we see. Similarly, smell and taste are processed, through a part of the brain in control of each.

The brain responds accordingly to what it likes and doesn't like. The nervous system is an intricate wiring system running throughout the body. Everything we touch and feel is transmitted through the nerves and processed in the brain. Is the object warm or cold, soft or rough, comforting or hurtful, to name a few. Pain is vital to knowing there is something wrong or hurting a part of the body. Feeling pain and the intensity is controlled in the brain.

What is even more interesting is how the information is processed and how the necessity to remember on short-term or long-term basis is determined; for instance, remembering the quote in a movie yet not recalling the title. How can we do so well on a quiz yet not recall the information on the final exam? Why do many of us struggle with remembering names?

Epilepsy

As a mentor and counselor, I am often asked, "What is epilepsy?" and "What is the cause?" Epilepsy is diagnosed when a person has two or more seizures that are not considered a side effect to a drug or explained by some other cause such as alcohol abuse or emotional trauma. A seizure is an electrical storm in a part of the brain that becomes overwhelmed, leading it to stop working temporarily. It may affect a small part of the brain or spread throughout all of it. During a seizure, various sections of the brain are impacted, and functional abilities are lost or distorted. It affects many people as their abilities are limited by their ignorance and fear of a seizure, whether they are the person with epilepsy, their caregiver, or the people with whom they come in contact.

Epilepsy is a seizure disorder that has been known for thousands of years. Sophocles wrote of it, and people such as Alexander the Great and Julius Caesar had epilepsy. In ancient Roman society, a person with epilepsy was highly respected because seizures were thought to be a way the gods communicated with people. Caesar's greatest fear when leading men into battle was not the outcome of the battle; it was having a seizure that would make him incapable of leading his men. There is debate about whether many of the prophets in the Bible heard voices or attributed to God or saw visons because of temporal lobe seizures.

In the Middle Ages, and in some cultures today, people were and are isolated from others because of the fear of seizures being spread through contact. Epileptics were considered possessed by demons and exorcism was practiced to make the demons leave the body. Although exorcism is not often applied, demon possession is still believed to be true today and practiced through some church organizations in the United States.* In reality, there is no demon, no possession, and no punishment by a god.

Brain Components and Development

The brain has five major components referred to as lobes. Each lobe performs a basic function with body senses and memory. The frontal lobe is the basis of memory, behavior, movement, and intelligence. The parietal lobe is the center of language, sensation, and reading. At the back of the brain is the optical lobe, and it is associated with vision. The cerebellum is at the base of the brain and controls balance and coordination. The center of behavior, hearing, speech, vision, and memory is through the temporal lobe.

There is a series of structures and glands that tie the lobes together and affect various components of the body. The limbic system is the center of emotions and includes the amygdala, hippocampus, hypothalamus, and thalamus. The amygdala controls rage and emotional responses, and the hippocampus affects memory. We have right and left hippocampi and amygdala and can usually remove one without changes in effect; memory associated with verbal information goes down slightly with removal of the left dominant hippocampus. Like a computer RAM, the hippocampus assorts the information presented through the senses and stores it in the cerebellum. Then, when the need arises, it pulls it back.

The brain is made up of a network of wires known as neurons and is the control center of the entire body. It consistently develops and changes to meet the requirements of what it is programmed to do. In early childhood, it develops the fundamentals in life such as eating, tasting, talking, identifying, to name a few. It is the actual connection or sequencing of neurons as they come together or detach to create the memory of an event or emotion. It is fascinating to watch infants wanting to touch and taste everything. When they do not like how hot or cold the item is or how it tastes, they remember not to touch or taste them again. Although someone can tell them what will happen, it will not register in the brain until they experience it. This often continues well into early adulthood. This follows the old cliché of "Most people don't believe the paint is wet until you touch it."

In the adolescent stage, there are more changes as the child learns to associate with people outside the home and discover their interests and abilities. Often the answers to a question, especially when asked by a parent, is a delayed "Yes," "No," or "I don't know." The

---

* This is based on the Bible verses of Matthew 17: 15-18, Mark 9: 17-27, and Luke 11: 38-42 explaining how Jesus provided healing by removal of a demon. This fit the culture of the time and the people's inability to comprehend the organs of the body, let alone the brain.

delay is often due their brains for searching for the answers. The problem is many children cannot respond in total because their brains are going through a significant change in development.

Then there are the emotions—those feelings and responses to what happens around us. For some of us, crying or laughing comes at an appropriate time, and we fit in with the rest of the group. Not everyone responds the same way. A few cry when others laugh, and for some, they do not know what it is like to do either. How does one learn to control feelings, especially when they are overwhelmed by them?

The center of the brain that controls the emotion of fear is known as the amygdala, all animals have this, and it is essential to survival. The amygdala is the size of a large pea, and there are two of them—one in the left and one in the right hemisphere of the brain. When fear becomes the dominating feeling, it takes one into the dark side of life, feeding depression and anxiety and preventing a person from moving forward. The amygdala is a very active part of the brain for people living with epilepsy.

Medical Perspective

From a medical perspective, epilepsy is diagnosed when there is more than one occurrence of a seizure with a neurological disorder in the brain. The cause is often unknown; however, in many cases, the cause may be from a high fever, infection, or head injury. These situations often cause enough injury to leave lesions (like scars) within the brain. A medial temporal lobe seizure is one of the most common forms of epilepsy. It is often caused by a major injury such as meningitis or head trauma.

As a young child or adolescent, it is not unusual for the brain to outgrow or sufficiently develop in the problem area and the seizures stop. This often takes years, and the person may never have another seizure. However, prolonged seizures occurring prior to the age of four and followed with additional head injury creates more scarring in the brain, resulting in seizures forming by the teenage years.

With older adults, the brain aging and degenerating may signal an onset. A lack of blood flow to the brain caused by a heart defect or the arteries from the heart becoming restricted may also cause a seizure, especially in women. Strokes are often the cause of seizures in older adults.[*]

Seizure Stages and Types

There are three stages to a seizure: the preictal, ictal, and postictal. The preictal stage is when a person is cognitive of what is around them, yet they have an odd feeling, taste, premonition, déjà vu, or sudden motion with a hand or foot.

The ictal stage occurs as the seizure intensifies and continues to spread over parts or all the brain. At first, the person becomes quiet, motionless, and stares straight ahead. Then

---

[*] There are two categories of strokes. A hemorrhagic stroke involves bleeding in the brain. Ischemic strokes are the most common and relate to blood clots that cut-off blood flow to part of the brain.

depending how far the seizure spreads, the body may stiffen and shake as the muscles tighten, sometimes to a point where they are injured by tearing. Breathing may stop temporarily. Some people may urinate and vomit, chew, grind their teeth, or clap their hands. Some of the more difficult cases may involve the person running or walking while oblivious to what is really happening. This phase is often the most difficult to watch and may leave memories instilled on the caregiver's mind.

The postictal stage starts when the brain resets and the person begins to regain control. This may last a few minutes or take days to fully recover. When I had seizures that started in my left temporal lobe, my ability to speak would take several minutes to a few hours to return, and to fully assemble thoughts could take several days. After surgery, total recovery took only a few hours.

There were only two known types of seizures when I was diagnosed with epilepsy in 1964: petit mal and grand mal. Through medical research, according to the Epilepsy Foundation of America, seizures have now been identified and categorized into three major groups[*]:

1. *Generalized onset seizures* affect both sides of the brain or groups of cells on both sides of the brain at the same time. This term was used before and still includes seizure types like *tonic-clonic*, *absence*, or *atonic*, to name a few.[†] There are two categories of symptoms:
   - Motor symptoms may include sustained rhythmical jerking movements (*clonic*), muscles becoming weak or limp (*atonic*), muscles becoming tense or rigid (*tonic*), brief muscle twitching (*myoclonus*), or epileptic spasms (body flexes and extends repeatedly).
   - Nonmotor symptoms are usually called *absence seizures*. These can be typical or *atypical absence seizures* (staring spells). Absence seizures can also have brief twitches (*myoclonus*) that can affect a specific part of the body or just the eyelids.

2. *Focal onset seizure* has replaced the category of *partial seizures, because,* the term *focal* is more accurate when talking about where seizures begin. Focal seizures can start in an area or group of cells in one side of the brain. Focal onset seizures are categorized based on the person's level of awareness during the seizure. This includes:
   - *Focal onset aware seizures* occur when a person is awake and aware during a seizure. This used to be called a simple partial seizure. Motor symptoms may include jerking (*clonic*), muscles becoming limp or weak (*atonic*), tense or rigid muscles (*tonic*), brief muscle twitching (*myoclonus*), or epileptic spasms. There may also be automatisms or repeated automatic movements, like clapping or rubbing of hands, lip-smacking or chewing, or running.

---

[*] The EPILEPSY FOUNDATION OF AMERICA, and EPILEPSY FOUNDATION are federally registered trademarks of the Epilepsy Foundation of America, Inc. The information is from their website; https://www.epilepsy.com/learn/types-seizures.
[†] More information concerning the types of seizures may be found in Appendix C.

- *Focal onset impaired awareness seizures* occur when a person is confused, or their awareness is affected in some way during a focal seizure. This used to be called a complex partial seizure.
3. *Unknown onset seizures.* When the beginning of a seizure is not known, it's now called an unknown onset seizure. A seizure could also be called an unknown onset if it's not witnessed or seen by anyone. An example is when a seizure happens at night or when a person lives alone. As more information is learned, an unknown onset seizure may later be diagnosed as a focal or generalized seizure.

Electrical Storms of a Seizure

The brain consists of a bundle of nerve cells. Those that makeup the outer part of the brain are referred to as the cortex. These nerve cells, known as neurons, have transmission fibers called axons that form the deep part of the brain, also called white matter, and are lined with a fat-rich insulation called myelin. Any injury that causes nerve tangles in the cortex can cause abnormal electrical transmission between nerves. When these get synchronized—discharge in rhythm—then seizures consisting of abnormal electrical conduction across the brain's nerves can start.[*]

When a neuron gets overloaded, it passes the impulse onto other neurons. As more neurons become excited, the region of the brain they are in becomes overloaded and impacts the section of the brain it is associated with, such as emotions or the ability to move body parts. As this overload passes to more neurons, the result can lead to sections of the brain becoming inoperable, especially the areas that are damaged and tangled. This is known as an "electrical storm" created as the nerve's cells are firing too quickly.

A way to understand the impact of damaged neurons for those who have never had a seizure is comparison with a computer system. There are the times when the computer suddenly stops working and the screen goes blank. A few seconds later, everything seems to be working fine, except there is missing data such as the information that had been typed in just prior to the screen going blank. In a sense, the computer had a partial complex seizure where major functioning components shut down momentarily and the memory was impacted.

There are series of chemicals that control the activity of the nerve cells. Chemical imbalances in the brain are often caused by physical changes in the body and what is consumed. There are four categories of chemicals or neurotransmitters in the brain, glutamate, serotonin, gaba, and dopamine. Glutamate is an excitatory neurotransmitter, serotonin effects mood, gaba slows thing down, and dopamine effects motivation. AED's impact the level of one or more of these neurotransmitters to bring control to the neurons and seizures. Neurotransmitter imbalances are caused by stress, hormones, aging, diet, injury and illegal drug use. The difficulty is to determine which AED is most applicable to obtain the proper balance. It may be necessary to try several AEDs and dosages before finding the one or several needed to control the seizures. This

---

[*] Provided by Dr. Krauss of Johns Hopkins Hospital.

is a continuous process as the body ages or adapts to the medication to the point the AED is no longer effective.

Seizures and the Senses

A person's five senses and responsiveness are affected by where a seizure begins. Some people have seizures that start in the occipital lobe, and their vision is impaired. If the nerves continue to become overly excited, the seizure spreads to other sections of the brain and affects their other senses and abilities.

If seizures begin in the hippocampus, the memory is affected. Often, the seizure spreads to the areas close by, impacting vision, speech, and hearing. The centers of speech and memory recover slowly, and although the person can talk, their ability to comprehend and remember takes more time to fully recover. They can be more fearful of what is happening around them, or they will no longer laugh and play. Their inability to recall or recognize words may interfere with speech and reading skills.

Seizures may occur in the part of the brain that effects smell and taste. Suddenly smelling something that is not near you or having a taste with nothing in the mouth can be due to a seizure, but more often these are memories of what you had (or hope to have) for a meal or remembering a smell of something a person came close to.

When a seizure starts in the occipital lobe, a person's vision is affected. Over-excitement of the nerves causes the seizure to spread across to various sections of the brain and affects other senses and abilities. Seizures that begin in the hippocampus affect the memory and often spread to areas that effect vision, speech, and hearing. So, although a person can talk, their ability to comprehend and remember what happens may take additional time to recover. They may be more fearful of what is happening around them, or unable to comprehend how to laugh and play. Their inability to recall or recognize words may interfere with talking and reading skills.*

When seizures involve only a few sections of the brain, a person's cognitive abilities may not be completely interrupted. A young woman had a seizure across the table from me. Her speech was interrupted, while she stared straight ahead. Her father, who was nearby, came over and started to talk to her quietly, reassuring her that she was safe, and everything would be okay in a couple of minutes. A few minutes later, her abilities fully returned as her seizure stopped and her brain reset. She was still able to see and hear while her seizure was occurring, even though she could not move her body or eyes.

Seizure Triggers

Changes in anti-seizure medication levels are a common cause for breakthrough seizures; therefore, the medication must be taken daily as directed by physicians without missing dosages to maintain the appropriate blood level. Missing a dose increases the risk of having a seizure, especially when a person does believe they do not need the medication anymore. It is also

---

* Often children are diagnosed with an attention deficit, anxiety, or depression disorder when this is occurring. An EEG may be helpful in determining the appropriate cause and treatment.

important to get the medication levels checked several times a year because a person's metabolism changes as they age. Being on the same medication for many years may lead to a decrease in the amount required to keep the same blood level.

Anti-seizure drugs (AEDs) may reach a toxic level in the blood based on how fast the body, typically liver or kidneys, can process or filter it out. If the filtering does not meet or exceed the intake of the medication, the level will increase over time and eventually become toxic and impact a person's cognitive and physical abilities. This may lead to seizures or seizure like symptoms and cause serious harm to the kidneys and liver.

The side effects of AEDs can be minimal to some, or it can be incapacitating or physically harming to others. Prior to starting a medication, the doctor should discuss the side effects with the patient. If the AED affects their personality, which is not unusual, the doctor should be notified immediately, and options discussed. There have been cases where a spouse or parent could no longer relate to their loved one due to the negative changes in personality. The happy and energetic person they once knew had now become angry or severely depressed since being on an AED.

Changes in stress and anxiety levels are a leading cause of seizures. There are two basic forms of stress on the body—the physical and mental. High levels of physical stress often cause seizures as the body becomes dehydrated and chemically imbalanced, especially when such stress is not occurring on a regular basis, such as overexertion when starting an exercise program. Exercise programs are very healthy for most people and effective in lowering physical and mental stress levels. However, starting slow and building intensity is necessary for anyone, even if they do not have to be concerned with having a seizure.

Increases and decreases in mental stress cause a change within the brain that affects the entire body. It is known that an increase in stress is a tripping point for a seizure, especially as a person begins to dramatize the situation, enabling their fear to increase. This is often exacerbated by the outcomes they imagine. It is not unusual for people with epilepsy that their worries about having a seizure and the outcome become the trigger. When such stressors are resolved, the fears go away, and the brain slows down as the dramatization ends.

Sleep deprivation is another common trigger. If a person cannot sleep, they should rest regardless. Staying away from caffeine and sugar is helpful. Worrying about the amount of sleep often keeps a person awake. Simply rest the body and the brain. If the brain is busy with thoughts, write them down so they do not have to be remembered anymore, they can be addressed the next day. Let nature take its course.

Stress and sleep deprivation often lead to exhaustion—another key trigger to seizures. Exhaustion is when the body has no energy and the stress is exacerbated with the inability to think clearly. Our bodies and minds need rest and time to recharge naturally.

Eating regularly and consuming fluids affects the body's chemistry and plays a role in seizure activity. Dehydration is a key factor, and eating three meals a day is important, especially meals that consist of nutritious foods. Fast-food hamburgers were a problem for me, so eating good quality foods with little to no preservatives is very important.[*] Drinking fluids is essential; water and drinks with lower sodium is very helpful.

For some women with epilepsy, their initial seizure occurred when they started having menstrual cycles. Although they may have a seizure at any time, they tend to be most susceptible just prior to menses.[†] Menopause has been a time when some women start having seizures as their body chemistry changes.

A seizure triggered by flashing light is known as photosensitive epilepsy. It is usually associated with a genetic form of epilepsy and is a rare condition. Many children love to play video games where there is a sequence of lights flashing in the two-dimensional view of the TV screen, enhanced to appear to be three-dimensional. The brain gets confused, and the flashing lights overwhelm a part that leads to a seizure. The special effects in movies often create similar conditions and may also trigger a seizure. I quickly learned when to close my eyes as my aura started. Through people I have met, I learned how swimming pools with reflective sunlight caused by the movement of the water are also key seizure triggers. The difficulty in determining photosensitive seizures is how excitement is a trigger, often exacerbated by the nature of video games.

Seizures often start or are triggered by an environmental condition, event, or setting. They may be simple—as the alternating sun/shade associated with travel, such as riding down the highway and the sun shining between trees—or complex, which involves multiple conditions. Traveling to a location away from home creates changes in the environment, including the water consumed, the types and sources of food, air temperature, and time zone. Any one or a combination of these may be triggers to a seizure. The person may be stressed about the reason for the trip and fear the manner of transportation, be it flying or riding in a car. Blood levels of medication may change due to the chemistry of the foods, adapting to time zones, and changes in physical activity. He or she may drink bottled water to help decrease the changes in the chemistry of the water and reviewing the impact to medication levels with a doctor is very helpful.

Not all triggers may be identified. As the history of an individual's seizures is kept and reviewed, the triggers may be identified and avoided. A person should keep a record of each seizure that includes notes on medications, diet, sleep, and stress during the previous twenty-four hours. There often is a pattern that may be avoided or minimized to reduce the risk.

A Seizure that is not Epilepsy

In some cases, a seizure can be a reaction to a drug addiction, a new medication, a change in dosage, or a chemical to which a person is exposed. These consist of medications associated with treating another part of the body and not for seizures.

---

[*] This may have been due to the excess use of monosodium glutamate for meat tenderizing, which affected the glutamate level, an excitatory transmitter, in the brain.
[†] Seizures associated with the menstrual period are usually due to drops in progesterone, which reduces seizures in the luteal phase right before menses. Progesterone replacement didn't help most women with this trigger.

During a work seminar on estimating cost and time for construction projects, the woman sitting next to me had a grand mal seizure. She was asking a question to the instructor when suddenly, she quit talking as her body went completely rigid. Her muscles were so tense that every part of her body was shaking. Her head pounded against the back of the chair, and she lost control of her bladder as she unknowingly urinated onto the floor. I quickly got behind her and placed my hands between her head and the back of the chair to create a buffer so she would not hurt her head. My associate got up and ran toward the door, shouting that he was going to the nurses' office to get help.

The next two minutes were very traumatic for everyone as the seizure continued and the woman could not breathe. Her body turned a shade of blue, with her lips becoming deep blue. There was nothing anyone could do during that period. The only part of the chair she had contact with was the front edge with her hips and the top of the back support where her head pounded against my hands. The back edge of her shoes was in contact with the floor as her body was perfectly straight due to all her muscles contracting. Her muscles were so tense they shook, causing her body to jerk in a steady rhythm. Eventually, her body began to go limp, and I could feel her heart beating rapidly through her neck. Yet she still did not breathe. I kept her airway clear by tilting her head back. And just as I was about to try resuscitation by breathing into her mouth, she coughed and took a deep breath. I can still replay it all in my mind.

Her eyes began to wander as she tried to figure out where she was and what had happened. Another associate helped me pull her back onto the chair. About this time, the nurse arrived with a wheelchair and took care of the woman. We later learned she never had a seizure before, and the cause was due to a change in a medication. She was never diagnosed with epilepsy.

After the nurse left, I looked at the instructor who had been talking to the woman when she had the seizure. My immediate response was "we can get started again." Then realized the instructor was very pale and had not moved since the seizure began. He was staring at the lady's empty chair. At this point, I told everyone, "Let's take a break and talk about what had happened." First aid was required for the instructor and several people attending the seminar.

I approached the instructor and quietly asked him if he was okay. He did not respond and kept staring at the empty chair. Keeping a calm voice while telling him that what he witnessed was the woman having a seizure was important. As this was explained to him, he was able to turn his body to face me. He calmed down when told the woman was going to be fine and was safe with the nursing staff. Other people in the class came up to the stage, wanting to allay their fears from what they had just witnessed. Everyone was surprised when they learned of my living with epilepsy and recovering from many seizures. This brought reassurance that everything was okay, and everyone agreed we should continue with the class. Continuing was important because it gave everyone something positive to focus on in lieu of the trauma they had just witnessed.

After class, one of the men told me about his twenty-year-old son who has epilepsy. Like myself, the child had a high fever at the age of five. His fever lasted considerably longer than mine and caused more damage to the same section of the brain. In many ways, he remained a five-year-old because his mental development was severely damaged. We kept in touch for over fifteen years. Epilepsy can be traumatic for many people, the last time we talked he told me about his son's death, the boy was 28 years-old at the time.

Section 2
Personal Experience

Chapter 2
My Seizure History (1963–1968)

I have learned more about what my parents and siblings experienced with my first seizure as I work with the parents of very young children with seizures. Watching an adult have a generalized tonic-clonic seizure can be terrifying, especially with someone they love. I was four years old when I had my first seizure

First Seizure

It was not until years later that I learned more about the impact my seizures had on my parents and siblings. In 1963, I developed a high fever from influenza. It started during the night while I was asleep. I have no memory of what happened, so my sister Kathy wrote of her experience. She was eight years old at the time.

I would like to tell you my experience with your first seizure. I had faked being sick that day, so I didn't have to go to school. Mom had to go to the grocery store. She left us alone but told me Mrs. Small was going to stop by and make sure we were alright. It was getting late in the morning. I decided I needed to check on you to be sure you were alright. You were not alright. You were on your hands and knees in your bed unable to move. You could look at me. I was scared, but with the instincts of the future nurse I would become, I decided to check your temp. Needless to say, glass thermometers were the only way to go. I got the thermometer and begged you to open your mouth, which was clenched shut. Somehow you managed to open your mouth enough for me to slide the thermometer under your tongue. Your teeth clamped shut, glass and mercury went everywhere including the inside of your mouth. I thought I had killed you! I started screaming "Spit it out!! Spit it out!" I do not know how you did it, but you managed to spit it out. I went hysterical and went downstairs. I loved you and did not want you to die. Mom came through the door of the kitchen where she met me, still absolutely hysterical. I told her what I had done. She ran upstairs, got you, and left to take you to the hospital. As she left, she told me to call Dad and have him meet her at the hospital. The three days you were in the hospital, I worried. I did not want you to hurt or be sick. When you came home, I made sure you took your "little pill" whether I asked if you had taken it or whether I witnessed you taking it. I never wanted you to be sick like that again. I did not want you to hurt like that again.
I never faked being sick, again. Nor have I ever put anything in a seizing patient's mouth, again.

Keep in mind that cell phones did not exist at the time, and our mother could not be contacted as this was happening. She knew to get me to the hospital immediately. Kathy could remember the phone number of where our father worked and made the call. When we arrived at the hospital, I was unresponsive, my body began to shake, and became rigid. It was not until late afternoon that my fever broke, and I became semiconscious of what was happening around me. Although the fever had subsided and the seizure stopped, I was exhausted and slept for several hours. My parents feared the outcome, because no one could comprehend what I would be like upon waking up. Many years later, my mother asked if I remembered the first thing I said when waking up and regaining consciousness. I had no recollection. She said she would never forget it. I looked at her and said, "Mommy, I'm hungry."

To understand why this statement was so important is realizing what can happen to the brain during a very high fever. In some cases, a very high fever may lead to the brain overheating, causing lesions or scar tissue as the neurons become damaged. While at the hospital, my parents had been informed there could be some serious consequences to my mental abilities. No one knew what to expect until the seizure stopped and my system recovered. I was in the hospital for three days, being monitored for mercury poisoning. The three-day observation indicated that none was ingested. It was surmised that being in a kneeling position at the time my sister put the thermometer in my mouth caused the broken pieces of glass and mercury fall out. My mother found the mercury later in the bed. Two weeks after being discharged from the hospital, we visited a hospital specializing in epilepsy where an electroencephalogram (EEG) was performed.

First EEG

An EEG is a test where a series of wires are attached to the head to monitor the electrical impulses occurring within the brain. This enables the doctors to evaluate if someone has epilepsy and to attempt to identify the area of the brain that has been damaged. The damage is to the neurons that are more susceptible to become overloaded resulting in an electrical storm. The EEG is relatively simple and is typically completed within an hour. However, there are situations where the test may be done continuously over several straight days.

As a four-year-old, having a bunch of wires attached to my head, was terrifying, especially when I had no idea what was going on. The technician and my mother left the room, expecting me to take a nap. To this day, I can remember crying and shouting to my mother, "Do not leave me!" They both immediately came back into the room, and my mother assured me she was not going to leave me behind. Being a four-year-old, I thought something terrible was happening. It was more frightening because whatever they were doing, would mean being isolated from my parents, just like what happened every night while at the hospital a few weeks earlier. My mother quickly returned and assured me that she would not leave me behind, so I lay down and closed my eyes.

When the test was over, my mother and the technician returned to the room. Mom did not say anything, seeing her face brought a clear indication that something was wrong. The technician had shown her the results of the EEG, and they found an area where there was an electrical storm occurring in my brain. I remember how quiet my mother was, and she did not smile like she usually did. In fact, she did not say a word during our entire ride home. She was in shock as her four-year-old son had just been diagnosed with epilepsy.

Epilepsy is a condition that was, and still is, very misunderstood. People with it were often labeled and treated as mentally ill or unstable. In my parent's generation, people with epilepsy were sterilized to prevent the spread of the disease and in many cases, the child was placed in a special education group with children with learning disabilities.[*] Until the 1980's people with epilepsy were not allowed to marry in several states. The lack of knowledge about epilepsy and the social stigma of the time played a significant role in my mother's response to my diagnosis.

Medication Side Effects

In 1963, there were only a few medications available for treating epileptic seizures; the two primary medications available were phenobarbital and Dilantin. Phenobarbital was prescribed for me, which essentially slowed my brain down. When I was asked a question, I seemed to be unresponsive. The question would be repeated several times before I would provide an answer. My rate of speech had significantly slowed. My siblings referred to me as the old man because I acted like someone who was very old.

The energetic little boy who laughed and cried and did silly things as young children typically do was gone. My speech was slower than that of a typical child and was affected throughout my life. Fortunately, I was only on phenobarbital for four years. The doctors determined that an anticonvulsant was no longer needed because there had been no more seizures while on the medication, or so they thought. It would not be until years later that the déjà vu and my visions of bugs in the house were focal *onset* seizures with nonmotor symptoms.

Family Impact

The impact on the family was typical in many ways. The youngest of four required special attention during the child development years. My parents worried about what could happen if another seizure were to occur. And this concern, although not expressed, was passed onto my siblings. My brother, who was the oldest, became distant. He later went into medical research and teaching, with a focus on children with birth defects. The younger of my two sisters, who tried to take my temperature while having the seizure, became an emergency room (ER) nurse at a hospital and worked in this field for over thirty-five years. My oldest sister applied her creative skills in illustration to medical text and training programs. The two of us have a close relationship and grew even closer when she started having seizures. Initially diagnosed with epilepsy, she was eventually diagnosed with Meniere's disease. This is a condition that takes place in the inner ear, causing vertigo and loss of consciousness, similar to the seizures associated with epilepsy.

---

[*] In many cases the learning disability was caused by the AED and the impact to the memory and personality.

Seizure Reprieve

At the age of eight, four years after being diagnosed with epilepsy, the doctors decided the seizures were no longer an issue, and my medication was stopped. A whole new me developed, and new opportunities came into my world. Scouting provided some wonderful camping experiences, sailing helped me learn what to do when the unexpected happens, and my father taught me about working with my hands and engineering.

My father, who was an engineer, taught me about engines as we serviced his cars and lawn mowers. He taught me how to replace sinks and fix leaky pipes, rewire electrical circuits, and work with many tools as we did improvements to the house we lived in. I learned about being creative and how there are many ways to solve a problem. When something broke, he would first ask me what we should do to fix it. He would then refine my solution to what was needed. He taught me about brainstorming, taking what comes to mind when facing a challenge, then finetuning it to resolve the problem, a process considered to be an engineer's manner of thinking.

At the age of ten, I learned to sail a small boat on the Great South Bay, Long Island, New York. When I was fourteen, my parents bought me a Sunfish—a fourteen-foot sailboat that enabled me to sail over to Fire Island. I loved sailing because it provided independence and emphasized the beauty and power of nature.

Great South Bay is a special place, most of it is only two to four feet deep, and it is one of the largest clam beds in the world. I would sail for a while and then go to an area where I knew there would be clams buried in the sand. I would anchor the boat, step out into the shallow water, and find the hard shells of the clams by wiggling my feet into the sandy bottom. Upon feeling a clam, I would dive under, grab it with my hand, and drop it into the boat. The way home from the marina was by bicycle and a little challenging with a bucket of clams hanging on the handlebars.

The Boy Scouts, taught me about camping, backpacking, and most importantly, leadership. I attained the rank of Eagle Scout and did well in school. In 1976, a group of us went to Philmont, New Mexico, and backpacked 120 miles in some of the most beautiful country ever known. Just before graduating from high school and heading to college, I told my mother, "If I were to die today, it would be okay, because I have been able to achieve so much, and I've visited God's country."

Section 3
Student, Husband, Father (1977–2005)

Chapter 3
The University of Rhode Island

I found two types of people: those who care about me and those who fear me. With those who care, came a tighter bond. Those who feared me faded away. I still felt a sense of rejection

Soon after graduating from high school, I went to the University of Rhode Island and majored in civil and environmental engineering. It was exciting to be on my own, with an opportunity to earn a degree in engineering. There were many students on campus who were willing to help the new students to be ready when classes started. During the first week, there were events taking place to have people join one of the sports teams. My passion for sailing took me straight to the sailing team, where I quickly made new friends. I crewed for Brett and met Bill, who became an example for me on how to live with a disability.

Within a few months, the URI sailing team qualified for the Freshman Atlantic Coast Championship at the US Merchant Marine Academy, Kings Point, New York. The race was held in November 1977, with thirty-three colleges participating. Each had two teams as the races were separated into an A class and B class. Having the two classes enabled the crews to have a break between races to rest and talk with the coaches. Bill and another URI student were on the A team; Brett and I were on the B team. The boats were rotated through the teams, because any advantage to a particular boat would be only for one race, because it would be rotated through the other teams. Scoring was based on what place you finished in each race and the team with the lowest score was declared the winner. We finished in third place at the end of the program.

The first day was a sailor's nightmare, as there was no wind. We bobbed around the East River with an occasional light breeze and completed three races when usually there would have been six to eight races.

Sailing Accident

The second day, the wind was blowing 20 mph with gusts over 30 mph, and the temperature had dropped to just above freezing with an occasional snow shower. This was a college sailors' dream because, at that stage of life, we were invincible.

During what would become the last race for the A team, we watched our teammates crash, or flip the boat over. The tip of the mast bounced off the top of several waves, causing the forestay, the cable that held the mast up from the front to stretch a couple of inches. Bill and his crew managed to right the boat and complete the race. When they got back to the dock, Brett and I got in and sailed off. While we were waiting for the signal for the start of the next race, we noticed that the top of the mast was tilted toward the back of the boat several inches. This was due to the forestay becoming longer. We did not give a thought of this being an issue because we were so focused on ourselves and the chill we were experiencing. We had no warm gloves and did not wear much under our foul weather gear because it would get in the way. We were also

26

busy and tired from hiking out that required leaning our body weight over the opposite side of the sail to counter the force of the wind and keep the boat upright.

There was much maneuvering and fast course changes to get the boat in the best position as the horn sounded the start of the race. We were no longer concerned about the cold because we worked so hard that we were sweating like it was eighty degrees outside. We rounded the first mark in first place and took off like lightning, powered by the high winds. We were very excited and working so hard we had no time to be scared. We were now on a reach with the wind coming across the back of the starboard (right) side of the boat. This required both of us to get as far back as possible to keep the bow of the boat from plowing into a wave and flipping end for end. As we came to the second mark, we looked at each other very seriously knowing we were in deep trouble. There came the realization that due to the mast being tilted back so far, the boom was going to come very low into the back of the boat where we had to be as we made our turn. The turn we had to make now required changing direction with the wind coming from behind, leaving the sail continually under its power. The thirty mph winds would keep the main under a tremendous amount of power. Sometimes the main would start low and then snap upwards as the tension on the main sheet slackened while it came across the back of the boat. We were hoping this would happen, but it went the opposite way.

Brett was sitting on the back edge of the boat, and I was in the far back near the bottom of the cockpit. He pulled the helm over. And as he leaned back to get out of the way of the boom, he fell off the boat. His hand was so cold he could not let go of the tiller, and it caused the rudder to break off. I lay as low as possible. But as the boom came around, it snapped downward and slammed into the side of my head, then bounced up, and hit the water on the other side of the boat. Because neither of us could get into a position to counter the force on the sail the boat toppled over, and I was thrown into the water and the rigging. Within seconds, the waves caused the boat to go completely upside down.

I do not remember the boat flipping over and plunging into the water. Even after regaining consciousness, I was not able to move my body, but could feel my arms and legs. I was tangled in some lines, and Brett was pulling on the back of my foul weather gear. He yanked me out of the rigging and around to the back of the boat. He shouted, "Grab onto the rudder mount!" This was at the back of the boat where the rudder used to be. He hollered, but I could not hear him. Everything was in slow motion. The waves kept bashing us into the back of the boat, and he could not hang on.

I wanted to say something, yet the words were just not there. Eventually, my ability to hear and comprehend came back. Brett was holding onto me and the hull of the boat as best he could. Once he realized I could understand what he said and react appropriately, he helped me get to one side of the boat and hang onto part of the rigging. He then swam to the opposite side and pulled himself onto the hull until he could reach over and grab my hands so we could straddle the bottom by holding on to each other.

We did not know if we would be rescued in time. We were freezing and drifting very close to the Throgs Neck Bridge. As we lay there waiting for help, I saw my wool hat floating away. It was very thick, kept my head warm, and unknowingly cushioned the blow to my head. We were then washed off the boat hull by a wave. As the boat came down into the swell of another wave, we grabbed hold of each other and were lifted partly out of the water as the boat was raised to the top of the wave. We were tired, extremely cold, and struggling to hang on. When my ability to speak returned, I looked Brett in the eyes and sadly said, "I lost my hat."

Over the next several years, the first thing Brett would tell people when I introduced him was "We were about to drown, and all Jon was concerned about was losing his hat." I was sad to lose it, because it had saved my life.

After thirty minutes, we were picked up by one of the powerboats overseeing the race, and brought in. I was freezing, shaking uncontrollably, and was quite blue. The left arm of my foul weather jacket was missing, and the left leg of my pants had been ripped off. I was immediately taken to the showers where the warm water helped me regain my body temperature. Putting on dry clothes and a warm jacket felt wonderful, because being dry and warm again meant we had survived what seemed to be improbable.

We got to see the boat when it was brought back, and everyone was amazed at the amount of damage that had occurred; it was entirely destroyed. The hull was cracked from one end to the other, some of the rigging was pulled out of the hull, the jib was ripped in two, and the main sail was torn. The boom was badly dented and warped where it hit my head. The rudder was never found.

The side of my head seemed numb, so I was not aware of the huge knot and swelling on the left side of my head. The coach looked me over and asked if I would be okay during the two-hour ride back to the campus. I assured him that everything was fine. We climbed into the car, and I fell asleep, something that a person with a concussion should not do. In 1977 there was little information provided about concussions, about what can happen to a person and the need to seek emergency treatment. I would soon regret not obtaining medical attention.

No one realized the damage to my brain until the next day. I had to take a history exam that involved writing essays. I had most of the facts; however, the paragraphs and sentences were incomplete. I had started many sentences but never finished them. Within a few weeks, I was having odd feelings in my stomach, and my hands would shake. Eleven months later, I had a grand mal seizure.

First Grand Mal Seizure

After recovering from the head injury, came the periods of high anxiety, where my heart raced, and had strange nauseous feelings. The nausea would grow in intensity for a minute or two and then stop. I thought the anxiety was associated with my classes and assignments. In today's standards these would be described as a local seizure, even though consciousness was not lost. Once again, my ignorance prevented me from seeking appropriate care.

It was early October 1978, my sophomore year, and eleven months since the boating accident. I was determined to get a 4.0 or perfect grades this semester. It was a Friday afternoon, and there was approximately three hundred people with me in a lecture hall, taking an exam in dynamics class. We had one hour to complete four questions.

In the evening prior to the exam, I was unknowingly experiencing the preictal stage of a seizure. This included a tenseness throughout my body, high anxiety, inability to eat, and feelings in my chest and stomach like a wave of nausea. I could not sleep the night before and walked around the campus at 3:00 AM. Eating breakfast was very difficult because chewing food made me feel like vomiting. At lunch time, an hour before the exam, even thinking about solid food made me sick. Needing to consume something to keep my energy level up made me attempt to eat some soup at lunch time. My hand shook so much that eating with a spoon was impossible, so I picked up the bowl and tried to drink some of it without spilling. I had never been so tense and could not understand what was happening.

In the lecture hall, I sat in the front row of the balcony section and could see most of the people in the class. There were four problems requiring an explanation of the formulas to be used, then applying them in detail, and showing the answer. As I read each one, my anxiety increased to a state where my mind went blank. Eventually, I could remember some of the equations and apply them to solve three of the questions. The remaining was the Ferris wheel; that required evaluating the forces people experienced at various stages of the ride. By this time holding a pencil was nearly impossible and the only thing I could see was the exam itself, as my peripheral vision was gone. It was like zooming in with a camera, except everything along the edge went dark. The fear center of my mind was escalating.

The ictal stage was underway as the seizure spread to other parts of my brain, affecting my eyesight and making me stand up and scream. The exam documents seemed to float away, and suddenly everything went dark. My classmates were stunned as they watched me fall between the rows of seats and students. Those near me went into a state of shock as I vomited, and my body shook uncontrollably.

My tongue was clenched between my teeth, and blood was flowing out of my mouth. A fellow student grabbed a small notebook and popped my jaw open so he could slip the book between my teeth, then protected my head from the concrete floor. He knew how to do this because his father had epilepsy. Someone called the paramedics, and within ten minutes, I was rushed to the infirmary.

When I regained consciousness, the first thing I wanted to do was to complete the exam. I could now remember all the details necessary to solve the problem of the Ferris wheel—the one I could not remember how to do prior to the seizure. The craziness that had been ongoing in my brain was gone, and my body was calm, but hurt in several places from the impact and the muscle tear caused by the seizure. My head hurt a lot too. The doctor had seen this with many students who had seizures caused by the stress of college and not taking care of their bodies. He contacted the professor who was accommodating and waiting to see me when I was discharged. When the doctor learned of my history of seizures, with this being my first in fifteen years, he changed his treatment plan. It was not the usual case after all so he would not allow me to leave.

He called my parents' house to inform them of what happened, and to come immediately and take me home, to obtain appropriate medical attention.

My mother received the call, then immediately called my father, who was closer to the campus due to where he worked in Garden City, New York. He had a calm disposition and was always one of the last to leave the building; however, this time his staff saw him quickly tell an associate his son had a seizure as he ran out of the building. He set a record driving the 165 miles to the campus. While all this was happening, I was totally exhausted and slept until he arrived.

My dad smiled at me as he walked into the examination room, and I could hear the doctor telling him what happened. He was pleased to see I was able to talk and stand on my own. I was still wearing the shirt covered in vomit, so in lieu of heading straight home, we walked over to my dormitory room where I could shower and change my clothes. We were soon on our way back home. This time, my dad drove within the speed limit. During the four-hour ride, we talked about what I could remember prior to and after the seizure. I had a splitting headache, still felt exhausted, and slept through most of the ride.

Mom heard the car come into the driveway and ran outside to help me. She looked very worried and was afraid of what happened. She was having flashbacks of witnessing me have the seizure when I was four years old. While she waited, she called her friends, some of whom were doctors, and arranged for me to see a neurologist first thing Monday morning.

The neurologist concluded that the seizure was nothing to worry about and was probably just a very unusual occurrence. His instructions included not drinking alcohol and to be sure to take my medication. He prescribed Dilantin and had my blood level tested a few days later. The test was done every hour for eight hours to see how my body reacted to and processed it. I have been on Dilantin now for over forty years.

His recommendation was that I do not lose my driver's license. All this had occurred prior to 2008, when the Health Insurance Portability and Accountability Act (HIPAA) that became law in 1996, was revised to include people with epilepsy, and would have protected me from the doctor having to report the seizure to the New York State Department of Motor Vehicles (DMV). Three weeks later, a letter came from the DMV, notifying me that my license was suspended for a year. This was extremely frustrating because I had just refurbished a car, and now had to sell it. I called the agency and requested an explanation as to why the license was suspended when the doctor had not recommended it. After being told this was state policy and with no exceptions, I slammed the phone down and could not believe how rigid the agency was with people in my condition. I asked why this applied to people with epilepsy and no other serious conditions associated with heart attacks or strokes. After reviewing the situation with an attorney, it was decided legal action would take longer than a year, so it was best to wait it out.

Sail On

I never did give up sailing. In my junior year, I moved into a beach house near the university with my friends from the sailing team and continued to crew with Brett. The Windsurfer had just come out, and some people kept theirs at our house. I quickly learned how to sail a Windsurfer, and I loved it. Sailing taught me so much about survival and that I had to put my trust in God's hands. I found peace while sailing, powered by a force we cannot see and that can change at any time. There was a similarity to this with my brain and seizures. Most of the time, sailing is fun. It is when the storms come that you need to be in a safe place. Seizures were the storms that occurred in my brain and can come at any time. With sailing and seizures, I would not always be in a safe place when the storms occurred.

Second Seizure

Five months later, during spring break, I went sailing with several people from the sailing team in Florida. Although this involved loss of sleep, not eating regularly, and a significant change in the environment, there were no problems with my seizures. In fact, not having any stress from classes taking my seizure medication was considered optional—to take only if I felt a need to. We had been back on campus for less than a day when classes started. I experienced some anxiousness during my 8:00 AM class, but this was typical during the first few days after coming back from vacation. My next class was in psychology, held a small auditorium. Immediately after taking a seat, came an extreme feeling of anxiety. The nausea sensation came just a few minutes later and grew in intensity. My arms became weak, and my vision was partly obscured. I looked at the person sitting next to me and calmly told her, "Goodbye." I have no memory beyond this point; however, my high school girlfriend was in the class and witnessed everything. She even rode in the ambulance with me to the infirmary. This time, I did not vomit, nor did I stand up and scream as had happened with the previous seizure. I went rigid for a few minutes and chewed and swallowed in a rhythmic fashion. The post-ictal state left me in a comatose form of sleep. I did not know what happened until waking up a few hours later. Even then, I could not tell the doctor my name or where I was. It was the same doctor who took care of me after my previous seizure and recognized me instantly. He called my parents and my dad immediately was on his way to pick me up and take me home.

Basic Rules

This time I saw a different neurologist, and the visit had an impact on finally accepting my diagnosis of epilepsy. Just as my mother and I were called into the doctor's office, he received an emergency phone call. Over the next ten minutes, we watched him talk on the phone to a woman who was pleading for his help, crying. She had called from an emergency room where her husband was dying from a brain tumor. The neurologist kept telling her, "There is nothing else I can do for your husband. He is going to die." When he hung up the phone, he looked pale and firmly told me, "You have epilepsy." He knew I was not accepting of my situation, so he gave me the five basic rules in controlling my seizures. These included the following:

1. Eat appropriately and don't skip meals.
2. Get eight hours of sleep, minimum.

3. Keep yourself hydrated—no alcohol.

4. Stay physically active; don't overstress and be careful when you travel.

5. Take your medication.

He went on to say, "If you break one of the rules, you increase the probability of having a seizure. If you break two of the rules, you will probably have a seizure. If you break three of the rules, you will have a seizure. If you break any rule consistently, you will have a seizure!"

The most important part was taking my medication; if I broke this one consistently, I could always count on having a seizure. He then told me not to drink alcohol; however, being in college, he recognized that I probably would, so he gave me some basic rules about drinking and taking medication: don't take both at the same time. Within a few months, I conceded and stopped drinking alcohol altogether. When going to the bars with my friends, the bartenders usually gave me a soft drink for free. My role among my friends was being the sober one of the group to make sure everyone got home safely. The tough part was the clock started over on getting my driver's license reinstated. It would take another twelve months before consideration would be given by the DMV to reinstate my driver's license.

I had missed a week of classes, including a quiz, and had a lot of work to make up. The toughest part was the fear now developed in me about having another seizure. Would my ability to drive be revoked forever? Could I ever take another exam without my mind going blank and having another seizure? Would I ever be able to become an engineer? Depression set in as I struggled with the fear and consequences of seizures. I started asking the question "Why is this happening to me?"

A few days after returning to campus, my father sent me a letter addressing what he witnessed in me from the time he picked me up to dropping me off at campus a week later. He provided some guidance in dealing with tough situations, like the one I was in. In some ways, he could reflect on what I was going through because he was in a bicycle accident when he was twelve and nearly died from a head injury. His father had been notified by the police and was told to bring a pastor to the hospital to do the last rights. My father beat the odds and fully recovered. He wrote this:

Dear Jon,
When you left this morning, I felt you left quite reluctantly. This is quite understandable because home and parents represent a certain security that we all need . . .One of the key things in life that all of us must learn is that nothing is stable, everything changes. Some of the changes are for our betterment, some are not. The thing we must learn to do is adjust quickly to the situation, good or bad. Nothing is ever all good or all bad so if we want to be happy then we must find the good in all situations and concentrate on it. Otherwise one can become very bitter and/or disillusioned.

In the case of your seizures you no doubt have said to yourself, "Why me?" All I can say is "Who knows?" The Bible says the sun shines and the rain falls on the good and evil alike. All the evidence says this must be the answer to the question, "Why me?" Instead of worrying and being torn apart by, "Why me?" we have a better choice. That choice is "oh there is an obstacle in my path; how can I get around it, over it, under it, or through it? I will not give up my goals. If I have to modify the goals "OK" but as little as possible because I will get where I want to go . . .

All I want for you, Jon, is the good life and the only way I know to have the good life is to go forward. Sure, there will be setbacks and disappointments, but when they occur find a way to make up for what was lost and find the courage and drive to go forward again. If you do this I'm quite sure you will have a happy and full life.

Love,
Dad

This letter brought me a huge sense of relief and comfort. No longer was there a need to meet a standard I thought my parents wanted because it was impossible to live up to; a perfect class average of a 4.0 GPA was no longer necessary. Most important was being reminded how much my father loved me. He was my foundation in living through such difficult times. He inspired hope in me.

Driving without a License

We were at a college party and my friends had had too much to drink. Due to my medication, I had not been drinking or had any problems with seizures for several months, so it made sense for me to be the designated driver that night. Just as we were approaching a friend's house, the blue lights of a patrol car started flashing behind me, and we were pulled over by the police, because the taillights were off. When asked for my license, I was honest with the officer and told him that I did not have one and was driving because everyone else was intoxicated.

The officer did not believe me and had everyone get out of the car. With their adrenaline running, all but one of my friends could stand straight. The officer walked back to his car and reported the event to the dispatcher. While he was sitting in his car, the owner of our vehicle walked over to him and argued that I was telling the truth. I guess the beer on the fellow's breath, and the officer being trapped in his seat, convinced him that the people in the car were indeed unfit to drive. The officer realized what we had done was in the best interest of everyone and the safety of others on the road.

When the officer was finished with the call in, he came over to me and apologized for not taking me seriously. He felt bad, because the call had already been made to the station and could not be reversed. However, he was able to change the charge from "driving without a license" to "driving without a license on my person." The owner of the car got charged for the taillights. The officer directed me to never to do this again. He then told me to be safe and to drive everyone home. When this went to court, the judge could not believe the story, that a person got a ticket for doing the right thing. The fee was drastically reduced, but unfortunately the ticket would not be removed from my record.

Disabled

The seizures were well controlled over the next year, although I still had minor auras that are considered today to be simple focal seizures, the type where consciousness isn't affected. Because of everything that was happening in my life, including the states driving restrictions and the fact that several people in my classes who would no longer associate with me because they feared my seizures, I suffered from depression.

The person who kept me motivated was my friend Bill who suffered with some physical disabilities caused by his mother being on the drug Thalidomide during pregnancy. Although he could not run well, he was a great sailor. In a race, he usually finished in the top three. If he could live so well even with his disabilities, I knew I could live with my seizures.

My one-year driving suspension was over the end of my junior year. I got my driver's license back and felt like a free man again. Since my license was from New York, and I was now living in Rhode Island, I talked to the staff at a local satellite office of the motor vehicle department to learn about any restrictions for people with epilepsy. I was told there was no requirement for a doctor's certification every year as required in New York. I filled out the forms, answered the questions, and marked yes under diagnosed with epilepsy. I did not report being given a ticket the year before because of what happened with the judge. Without any questions about my seizures I was given a driver's license and felt a huge sense of relief.

Three months later, while enjoying the beginning of my senior year, a letter was received from the Rhode Island Department of Transportation. They informed me that my license was suspended, and that the tags were revoked on my car for lack of medical validation from my doctor that it was safe for me to drive. I was broken. I drove to the main office in Providence and met with the director. He apologized for the misinformation by the satellite office and said there was nothing else he could do. He was going to delay any issuance of a license until a letter was received from my doctor validating my ability to drive based on my failure to report receiving a ticket the year before.

Suicidal Ideations

I left his office and was overwhelmed and sat down on a chair in the waiting area, buried in a sense of desperation and hopelessness. While thinking of what I could do to get the DMV to listen to me, the first answer that came to mind was to cut my wrist and wishing that I had a knife on me. As soon as I thought this, I heard a voice scream out *no*. It was like a slap in the face that brought me back to consciousness—the realization that to follow that route of punishing those who hurt me, meant being totally defeated by the system. I was not going to let that happen. The challenge was established: I was to learn to survive such dark times.

The following weekend, I hitchhiked to New London, Connecticut and rode the ferry to Orient Point on Long Island, then hitchhiked to my parents' house in Bay Shore, New York. I was deeply upset and needed someone to listen to me. My dad told me about the discrimination people diagnosed with epilepsy faced, especially with employment. He said, "If you want to work as an engineer, you cannot tell anyone about your seizures." The time away from Rhode Island and being able to still be mobile by hitchhiking was helpful in my recovery and he drove me back to the university the next day.

A few days after returning to college, I was waiting for a ride home at the entrance to the university. Waiting gave me more time to feel sorry for myself and fed my anger. The waiting also allowed me to notice, right in front of me, etched in a large rock, the Rhode Island state seal. The epiphany—a moment in my life that changed my perspective of everything that was happening, came like a slap in the face. At the top of the state seal is the word *HOPE* with the symbol of an anchor below it. Hope is key to pulling anyone through a tough or dark time in their life and having just an ounce of it would pull me along too. It is the anchor to the soul and provided a sense that God had never given up on me, and that I should never give up on him. I discovered the source of the "courage and the drive" my dad had written about in his earlier letter to me.

Encounter with an Angel

Once the appropriate documents had arrived from my neurologist, my driver's license and vehicle registrations were reinstated. It did not take long because there was a very short line where the driver's license was issued, and they had mine ready to hand back. Then there was no one else in the room where the car plates were distributed, except for the receptionist. As I approached him, he said, "I recognize you" (even though we had never seen each other). He smiled at me and said, "I have something special for you." He was gone for a few minutes and came back with a license plate with my initials on it. Apparently, when the story of my predicament got around the agency, this man took the time to order a special set of plates for me. This didn't sink in until a few days later. It made me wonder if he really worked there, because his action was beyond the ordinary. Maybe this was a simple act of kindness by a state employee. Then again, maybe he was an angel looking out for me, or both.

Seizures and Sailing

In the summers between classes, I lived with my parents. To help pay for some of my college expenses, I got a job as a groundskeeper on an estate that was within biking distance. They also allowed me to keep my boat there and continued to sail on Great South Bay. Eventually, I owned a Flying Junior—a two-person sailboat that was rigged for racing with a mainsail, a jib, and a spinnaker. With it, I learned a lot about how a boat reacts to an adjustment to the sail trim or other parts like the centerboard, which could be raised or lowered by adjusting one of the lines. Bill gave me an oversized spinnaker that made the boat nearly come out of the water as it flew downwind. The spinnaker taught me about pushing my limits, as often the boat seemed to be on the verge of flipping over. Although it was designed for two people, I often went out on my own.

There were times when I would lose control of the boat and would flip over, or as we liked to say, crashed. It was a moment when everything seemed out of control—a time requiring maintaining control of my emotions to regain control of the situation. With the boat laying on its side and the sails in the water, I needed to find and apply all the resources available to help right it again. Although the wind knocked the boat over, the wind could serve as the tool to lift it back up. The key was to point the mast towards the wind; then climb onto the centerboard and feel the boat start to come upright. My weight was only enough to get the mast to come out of the water however, this allowed the wind to get underneath it and provide the push needed to lift the sails out too.

Like any challenging life event, the situation required one to conduct an immediate assessment of what happened. The sails had to be cleared, the lines separated, and the water bailed out. The sails would flap in the wind, making lots of noise, and the lines used to trim the sails would flap around and cause the blocks to bang against the deck. Knowing how to sail and where everything had to be made recovery easier. Within a few minutes, I would be underway again, doing a review of what happened and what was learned from it, not only about the boat but also about myself. Later, when the seizures came back, sailing became a challenge because of another fear to be overcome; not of drowning, but the fear of seizures.

Many times, an aura (preictal stage of a seizure) occurred prior to sailing and generated a fear of getting on the boat. Once underway, my fears were abated because of having to pay attention to the boat and the wind. I could not see the wind; however, I could feel it, and sensed the power as it made ripples on the water and powered the boat. It was a power that cannot be controlled—only respected. It was in such times I felt closest to God. The government may have been able to keep me from driving, but it could not stop me from sailing. Sailing gave me an inner strength to face reality and ingrained confidence in me.

The people I did not consider during all this were my parents. They let me continue to take the boat out even though they feared what would happen if I had a seizure while sailing, especially alone. Years later, my mom told my sister Susan how when I left the house she would be filled with worry until my return. My parents never restricted me form sailing because they knew it was my manner of proving that I could still be me.

Eventually things were looking up, I earned my bachelor's degree in civil and environmental engineering in four years and graduated in 1981. I made dean's list several times, and people who got to know me learned why I talked slower than most. It was not because of low intelligence, as many first assumed, but because of the damage to my brain and the effects of the ASD. My abilities were tested several times. For me, the courses that centered on mathematics and the sciences were the easiest, the hardest were the English and History, the ones that required memorization and extensive writing.

A few months before graduation the Navy offered me a job at the shipyard in Charleston, South Carolina. This worked out well because a friend from the sailing team had graduated the year before and became a nurse at the Charleston Naval Hospital. If I needed any support, she and her friends were there to offer it. This became crucial because after a few months of living in there, I had to have my wisdom teeth extracted. The nurses provided transportation and offered me a place to stay for a few days in case there were any complications. For several days, eating any solid food for me was impossible due to pain. After getting a ride to the oral surgeon's office the doctor proceeded with extracting all four of my wisdom teeth.

Suzanne, one of the nurses who offered to help, came to pick me up when the surgery was complete. When the technician came in to wake me up, they said, "Mr. Sadler [repeatedly], your wife is here to pick you up." As I sat up in the recovery room, I was dazed and bewildered—dazed by the anesthesia and puzzled on how I became married while having my teeth extracted. Suzanne told me that the doctor's initial prescription for pain medication had a high risk of triggering seizures. She reminded him of my condition and had the prescription changed. I thanked her for the help, and she laughed when told they thought we were married.

Overstressed

The wisdom teeth pain and surgery played a significant role in triggering my next seizure. It had only been two weeks since my surgery when conditions were perfect to go windsurfing in the ocean near where some of my friends lived. For nearly two weeks, I had been breaking the rules I had been told concerning seizure triggers, because the pain in my mouth before and after surgery impacted my ability to eat or sleep properly. Furthermore, I was tired, out of shape, and mentally stressed from the surgery.

My parents had come for a visit from New York and were on the beach with some of my friends and work associates. They were excited to be with me, meet some of my new friends, and see where I was living. I figured going windsurfing for a little while would assure them that I was doing well so they would not worry about me. They dropped me off at the end of the island allowing me to sail along the beach for a few miles to where they would be enjoying the sun and getting to know some of my friends and coworkers.

The wind was blowing off the beach, so the ocean was calm, reducing the physical activity typically needed when there were waves. Within fifteen minutes I realized how out of shape my body was as my arms and legs started to get tired from holding the sail in place. The aura began soon after, and I was still a quarter of a mile from the beach and a couple of miles away from everyone. When the auras came while sailing, they were typically stopped by concentrating on the boat and adjusting the sail to reduce the physical stress. This time, however, the aura kept getting stronger, and my arms were getting weaker, causing me to eventually let go of the sail. With nothing to hang onto I lost my balance and stepped off into the water. It felt like stepping off the edge of a cliff in slow motion. I could still see but my body would not react, and because I did not have a life jacket, I kept sinking.

That my arms and legs should have been moving to propel me through the water was a passing thought, as my body had seemed to switch off, with no concern about reacting to the situation. I became a third person, physically standing behind and looking through the window of my eyes in wonder of the water and the light. With no sense of touch or connection to the body, my arms seemed detached and drifting out in front of me. Instead of fear and panic, there was a total sense of peace as my body was suspended in the water, drifting down where there was no sound or anything to be afraid of, surrounded in tranquility. The water got darker as I sank deeper, and I had a calmness and feeling of not being alone. I was at perfect peace with what was happening and thought, *so this is what it is like to die.*

Contact through the Soul

That was when I heard a voice say, "Not yet, Jon. I have plans for you." Immediately my old state of consciousness returned, and my mind and body came alive. The third person state of mind vanished, and I instantly started swimming toward the light and the surface. My lungs felt like bursting since I had not taken a breath for some time. A panic alarm was going off in my head, and the instinct to breathe took over. A battle between reality and instinct was ongoing and eventually instinct took over and I started to exhale while still underwater. My vision must have been impaired preventing my ability to see the surface but saw only light. Fortunately, I broke the surface just before starting to inhale. My chest felt like someone had severely beaten on it as I breathed rapidly. I had no strength and struggled to swim.

Unknowingly my peripheral vision had not returned so my window of sight was greatly reduced. This made it difficult to find my Windsurfer and panic set in. It must have drifted or sailed away. Turning my body, I caught a glimpse of it and discovered that it was right behind me, less than an arm's length away. I grabbed hold and hung on until my breath recovered. Struggling, I pulled myself onboard and laid there trying to regain my strength and get reoriented.

Eventually, I could stand and tried to pull the sail out of the water. It felt as heavy as a log, but it eventually came upright. It took several more minutes before I could get underway. Everything was still out of focus. The shore appeared to be a light-brown blur; the upper part of the sail would be there then disappeared. My destination was still far away. My body was running very low on energy and my brain had not fully recovered, yet knew I could make it, because the voice inferred there was much more in store for me. With time my vision fully recovered, and the shoreline became clear. It seemed so far away that it felt impossible to sail in.

Fortunately, there were no waves that day and when the Windsurfer hit the beach, I fell off the board and crawled onto the dry land, exhausted. there was nothing left in me. I was several hundred yards from where my parents were and could not get up to walk to them. I collapsed and laid face down in the sand.

Seems like moms have a sixth sense. As my mom saw me coming onto the beach, she knew something was wrong and started running toward me. One of my housemates saw her take off and quickly followed. Here was a fifty-five-year-old woman outrunning a twenty-year-old college football player.

She knelt next to me and put her hand on my back. Reassuring me that she was there and would not leave me. She helped me sit up while my friend got the Windsurfer out of the ocean. He asked what happened, but no one replied as my speech was impaired and mom knew but kept quiet. I must have looked terribly pale and was unable to stand up. I was able to say that I did not feel well, and my mother asked my friend if he could carry the Windsurfer to the house for me. Eventually, I had enough strength to stand and walked back to the group. I slept on the beach for a while and then walked back to the house. That night, I told my parents what happened; my mother told me she already knew, as she had seen this before when I had auras at home. I did not say anything to anyone about the voice I heard until years later. *

My neurologist was right. I broke more than three of the rules and therefore had a seizure. Surgery, eating, sleeping, and dehydration were a primary setup for a seizure. The extent of that seizure was different from a grand mal, because I was still consciousness of what was happening but had a loss of motor control (focal or partial seizure). Ironically enough, it was fortunate as it restricted my breathing, enabling me to survive while underwater.

Mark and I were renting a house on the Isle of Palms because of our love of the beach and boating. It was the best bachelor pad as he had two powerboats we could water-ski behind and explore the waterways and islands. I bought a used sixteen-foot Hobie Cat—a small twin-hulled sailboat that we kept on the beach. I would take the Hobie out by myself on days of moderate wind, and Mark would go with me when it was blowing harder. On our second time out, we achieved our summer goal of coming off the top of a wave and have the boat become completely airborne.

We loved to water-ski and pushed ourselves physically. We had fun living near the beach and working for the Navy. We stayed within the realms of the guidance provided by the neurologist as we ate well, stayed hydrated, and made sure we took our medications. We understood the importance of sleep and got a La-Z-Boy chair to promote taking naps. Playing hard was an important way of relieving stress.

I never gave up windsurfing and in fact have had much fun with it. One evening I went down to the end of Sullivan's Island in South Carolina and went windsurfing in the harbor. It was a beautiful evening, warm and clear. The tide was coming in, the flow was getting stronger, and the wind became calmer. After turning the Windsurfer back toward the island, I realized the wind was not strong enough to overcome the tide. I became stuck, and over the next two hours was carried farther away from my launch point.

There was a beautiful sunset, and the night set in. There was no moon, yet the harbor was lit with the light of the stars. Such conditions were awesome to behold. However, frustration set-in because I was not able to sail home or get anywhere close without a good wind. Suddenly, the water lit up all around me as some creature circled around me and set off the photosynthesis of the plankton. For a moment my thoughts focused on being devoured, then I heard the blowing

---

* Thirty years later neurologist found that hearing such voices is common for people with temporal lobe seizures. Recent studies indicate a neurological link between religious experiences and epilepsy.

sound of the dolphins swimming around me. They were checking on me to make sure everything was okay. They did this a few times and once more filled me with the awe because of nature. Soon after they left, the wind filled in, enabling me to sail back to the island.

When I got home, my friends demonstrated how much they cared about me by chewing me out for not letting them know what I was doing. They became frantic as it got dark and noticed my Windsurfer was gone. They had contacted the coast guard and had the police send out a boat to find me. It felt good to be cared for so much.

Chapter 4
Husband/Father (1984–2005)

The most difficult part of having a seizure was watching my son talk to the paramedics. I felt hopeless, for I had no control over the rest of my body

I met the person who became my wife through some friends who often came out to my house. She kept hearing, through her associates, about a fellow named Jon who lived at the beach and had all kinds of boats. We met at a group outing through work. She was intrigued by who I was, and we started dating. We fell in love and got married a year and a half after we met.

She was an officer in the Navy, so I came under the medical system of the US Navy. This involved filling out the paperwork for a Navy dependent to obtain registration and services. The form started with the officer's name and rank. Under the section for the spouse, the form read "wife's name." I crossed this out and wrote *spouse* and then my name. At the time, the Navy was unprepared for female officers with dependent spouses.

The Navy doctors were great. They reviewed my case history and saw that I had not had a grand mal or partial complex seizure in nearly two years. They recommended, and I agreed, to be taken off medication. I was excited to be able to put epilepsy behind me. There would no longer be any issues with getting a driver's license or working as an engineer. I was going to be freed from effects of seizures and medications once more.

Our First Seizure

About a month later, I was to attend a work-related class held in the evening in downtown Charleston. I got home from work to have dinner and get ready to drive downtown to the meeting. For some reason, I was very worried about finding the place and being on time. This worry grew more intense while I was getting ready for dinner. I began to focus on the people I would meet that night, especially those in the upper management. Over the next hour, my fear intensified, and transformed into anxiety, my hands began to tremble, and I could not understand what was happening.

We had just moved into our new house, and while this was happening, we were sitting at the kitchen counter. My anxiety level reached a stage where it hampered my mobility. Then the nausea hit me, and the aura started. The counter was very unsafe for me to have a seizure because of the hard surface and the stools, so I tried to get to the couch. The aura rapidly continued to intensify, and my wife watched me collapse on the floor. My eyes were open but were not responding, and my face was distorted. I was chewing on my tongue, and blood was trickling out my mouth. When she tried to pull my mouth open to free my tongue, I unconsciously bit her, and now she required medical attention. She got up, ran to the phone, and called 911.

I do not remember biting her but do remember the paramedics arriving. I could hear them talking to my wife as they came into the room. They saw my body was a shade of blue from not breathing. They cut through my shirt, attached leads from a heart monitor, and gave me oxygen. I could not move but was aware of what they were doing. They asked me simple questions such as "What is your name?" and "Where are you?" but I could not respond. The questions registered in my mind but the answer and the ability to speak were not there.

I was in a different world. I could see light but could not move my eyes or relate to what I was seeing. After several minutes of talking with my wife and observation, the paramedics recommended transporting me to a local hospital. Parts of my brain had come out of the electrical storm the seizure caused and I could begin to comprehend what was happening, yet the storm was still inhibiting my ability to speak. My response came through shaking my head. A few minutes later, my speech began to slowly return, allowing me to say "no." They had me sign a form stating I did not want to be transported. My wife agreed because we did not want to go to a local hospital with the confusion it would cause with the Navy health care system. The paramedics then insisted my wife obtain medical assistance immediately to have her hand treated for the bite.

The paramedics were thanked many times for their assistance as they gathered their equipment and left the house. The oxygen helped boost my recovery. The seizure had sucked away all my strength and it was impossible for me to stand-up, let alone walk anywhere. Sitting on the floor and leaning against the wall enabled my mind to continue to reset and to realize what had happened. The seizure caused me to lose control of myself and my wife saw a dark side of the person she married. I lost control of my emotions and cried hard because this meant that the battle within my brain would continue for the rest of my life. My wife knelt beside me and held me. She was scared too.

An hour later my body had recovered enough for me to stand and get ready to go to the navy hospital. I was weak and sore all over but was able to wash the blood off my face and change my clothes. My wife drove us to the emergency care unit at the Navy hospital, where they did an examination and gave me some anti-seizure medication, then scheduled an appointment with my doctor for the following day. The doctors seemed more concerned about treating my wife because the bite from a human can cause serious infections. She was given medication, and the wound was treated. As we drove home, I fell into a deep state of depression with the uncertainty what was going to happen next. Dread filled my mind as I thought about my what my wife was going through and the potential of losing my job.

Navy Doctors

The first thing we did the following day was see my doctor at the Navy hospital. His first comment was "Looks like we [referring to him] made a mistake."* My medication (Dilantin), was reintroduced and my mouth was checked over again. I asked about being reported to the state motor vehicle department, losing my driver's license, and the restrictions regarding working in construction. He assured me there was nothing to worry about since the Navy did not come

---

* Although I had been having auras at the time, no one correlated these as a form of seizure, for they had no impact to my cognitive abilities. Such auras are now considered to be a focal onset aware seizure that requires treatment.

under the jurisdiction of the state. A thirty-day driving restriction was required to ensure my medication reached an appropriate level to control my seizures. A letter was provided to give to my work supervisor concerning my absence and driving restriction. As I was getting ready to leave the room, it was highly recommended to me not to push myself for a couple of days to allow my body to recover.

The next stop was to see my supervisor at work. After explaining the situation and providing the letter from the doctor, he expressed his concerns about my welfare and assured me everything would be fine. He made arrangements for me not to have to drive and expressed his willingness to help in my recovery. Then he called the chief of the inspection team in and explained that the inspectors needed to help me continue what I typically did—visit construction sites. Psychologically, it was the best thing anyone could do for me. He did not want me to just sit in the office and isolate myself. Knowing that I could still be an engineer and continue to work eased my worries and cut off the adrenaline such anxiety could generate. Exhaustion set-in as my wife drove us home. Now we were to concentrate on my physical recovery. Everything that happened that morning brought peace that enabled me to fall into a deep sleep.

I took another day off and then had the weekend to recover. On Monday, one of the inspectors took me with him to review some work he was overseeing. We stayed in the safer areas of the site—ground floor of a building—just in case I had another seizure. The work was nearly complete, and no equipment or hazards were present. We then drove by some sites where we could review the initial phases of construction from his vehicle. Things began to look promising as the people I worked with were concerned about me and willing to help. My fears of how others would respond to my seizures diminished, and my depression melted away.

Contract with God

While learning about construction contracts, it seemed a good time to make a contract with God. I promised to continue to do my best, with the skills I was blessed with, and be a good person to others, but to do so would require control of my seizures for twenty years. He seemed to agree, and my seizures were controlled over the next six years. Everything was going extremely well with my relationships, employment, and physical and mental abilities. My weekends were spent on the water or at the beach with my wife and friends. I had terrific health care, and my supervisor was very supportive. There was no need to worry about losing my job if a seizure happened again. Life was good!

When my wife completed her obligation with the Navy and moved to Philadelphia to go to graduate school. My next assignment with the navy was to go to Mobile, Alabama, and be the resident engineer in charge of construction of a new naval station. Soon after my wife started graduate school, the Navy considered cancelling the work in Mobile. After several months of waiting to know if the cancellation was going to happen, I decided to move to Philadelphia and transferred to the Northern Division of the Naval Facilities Engineering Command in Philadelphia, Pennsylvania.

We were apart for four months until the transfer would go into effect. To stay busy, I planned to take the Professional Engineer (PE) Exam. This was my third attempt and was much better prepared with notebooks organized by subject with appropriate equations, tables, and example problems. My biggest fear was having no one with me in case a seizure occurred, which could be driven by the stress involved with exams triggering my seizures in college. Several auras occurred during the exam, but I finished on time. A few months later, the board notified me that I had passed, and we were very excited. This opened opportunities to many high-level positions within the Naval Facilities Engineering Command.

Seizures in Philadelphia

The stress of living alone was causing me to have more auras, and moving to Philadelphia, and changing jobs intensified the stress. Within a few months of relocating, a complex partial seizure hit me. I was playing racquet ball with a friend at an indoor facility on campus. The ventilation system was broken, and the court was hot, and the odor reeked of other people who had been playing hard and sweating profusely. We had just started to play when the aura started. This time the nausea was more intense than usual, and I could feel it in my arms too. My heart was racing. I immediately told my friend I had to leave and ran out the door. Running off the court and walking down a series of steps was the last thing remembered doing. My memory came back after returning to my apartment.

My friend told me I seemed to be walking fine; however, I was babbling, and he could not understand me. He accompanied me and as we came outside, I continued to walk straight onto the busy street. He grabbed my arm, pulled me back, and led me to his car. I did not seem to know how to get in, so he opened the door and guided me in. He was unsure if he should take me to an emergency room right away or not. Then he realized Becky would know what to do, so he drove back to the apartment complex we lived in. When we arrived, he guided me out of the car and up to my apartment. I have no memory of any of this.

Becky explained my epilepsy and thanked him for his helping me. Her assurance that I would recover helped him calm down. He felt much better about the situation, but wearied by the experience, so he walked over to his apartment nearby. I was exhausted and slept for several hours. Because of my need to drive, I could not obtain appropriate medical care. My stress level increased because of the seizure breakthrough and the knowledge that they were not totally under control. The only way for me to overcome the stress and the fears was to continue living and play by the rules the neurologist had given. This seizure came because of not paying attention to the environment, but no one could have known that at the time.

The following weekend, we played squash again—only this time there had not been anyone on the court before us, and the ventilation worked. I had no problems and could continue to play the game. My friend was much relieved, too, especially because he won this time. He laughed when told my obligation was to let him win after what he had done for me. We played many more times together, and I never had another seizure during a game.

Living in Baltimore

When my wife finished her degree, we moved near Baltimore, Maryland, and shopped for a house. Within a year, we found a nice place to live. We were excited with our marriage, work, and new home. A few months after we moved in, we both got a case of the flu, had fevers, and felt miserable. I had not been able to eat, drink, or take my medication for over two days.

My low-grade fever suddenly spiked, leading to two grand mal seizures in one day. When the auras started, I laid down on our new couch (the only piece of furniture we owned for our living room at the time). My wife was close to me and both times the first thing seen when coming out of the seizures and regaining some consciousness. There was nothing she could do except watch, help me take ibuprofen, and hope the fever would break. Early that evening, the fever went away, and no more seizures occurred. It would take several more days for my mental abilities to fully recover and was apparent in my difficulty assembling words. I would start to say a sentence and not realize I never completed it.

Positive Attitude Dissolving

I felt some form of control of the seizures as long as I could determine the trigger or cause. New doctors, new medications, and more knowledge of what we were dealing with helped me keep a positive attitude. I left civil service with the Navy and started working for a construction firm in Baltimore. This was very challenging and stressful as we had very tight schedules and budgets to meet.

The stress associated with the new job was getting to me, leading to several minor seizures a week. This was exacerbated by the stress of being dependent on a coworker for transportation. Our first child, Wesley, as a newborn, often affected my sleep, so the rules about sleep deprivation and stress were being broken.

With my seizures so out of control, my internal medicine doctor told me to go to Johns Hopkins Hospital to see if they could provide treatment to get the seizures under control. I was terrified, because this meant my seizures were so intense, I now had to seek medical care from one of the leading epilepsy research facilities in the world. After the initial testing and evaluation, my treatment involved several medications. Although they seemed to stop the seizures, the side effects severely affected my ability to mentally process information. This affected my family and work, and I decided it would be best to seek a second opinion. I started seeing another neurologist at a different hospital whose approach best fit my situation. I would return to see Dr. Krauss at Johns Hopkins fourteen years later when my seizures became intractable, meaning they were no longer capable of being treated with medication.

Finding Proper Care

The first visit to Dr. Johnson's office was in the early spring of 1991, Becky and Wes were with me. Wes was a few months old, and we carried him in a car seat designed for infants. When we entered the doctor's office, Dr. Johnson had us put Wesley on the end of his desk.

While talking about the types of seizures we were dealing with, the doctor's eyes became more focused on Wesley, and he began to get pale; a deep expression of sadness came over his face. When presented with my history of seizures, he took his eyes off Wes, breathed a sigh of relief, and said, "You're the one with epilepsy. I thought it was your child you were referring to. I can help you." This made me feel Dr. Johnson would be the best for me because he was open and willing to work with me as an individual. He became my neurologist during the next twenty-five years.

Now the fear of losing my job and not being able to take care of Wesley because of a seizure was becoming a dominate factor in my life. A few months after the appointment, Becky had to go out of state for three days of training, and I was going to be a single parent for that amount of time. As she was getting ready to leave, I took Wes for a walk. We were less than a block away from the house when I broke down. I was overwhelmed with the fear of having a seizure and could only imagine the worst outcomes. Soon after Becky left the house for her trip, I looked at Wes, and he smiled at me. This time my eyes were filled with tears of joy. The next three days were focused on him and not me, and my fears with epilepsy dissipated.

It seemed that every time a breakthrough seizure happened; a new medication was available for me to try. Most worked of them worked very well for a few years. When minor breakthrough seizures occurred, my neurologist would prescribe a new medication. Dilantin was the baseline and the new medications were secondary. When reactions to medications occurred, either physically or mentally, there seemed to be another recently developed that I could try that minimized my seizures for a few more years.

Wes became aware of and was concerned about my seizures at a very young age. Some of his earliest memories came from seeing me have one. I kept trying to get him to say his name in case one should occur while we were away from home. He seemed to be very serious and did not say anything for over two years. In fact, we thought there was an issue with his mental development. One day while we were outside eating dinner on our deck, a fly started pestering us. I tried to kill it by clapping my hands together as it flew in front of me. Some of Wes's first words came as he said, "Uh oh, Daddy." He thought I was having a seizure, because clapping my hands often happened during the ictal stage. He had sensed something was wrong.

Limits

Going sailing still had a calming effect on me. To help manage my stress, I volunteered to crew on a thirty-four-foot sailboat in a regatta held every Wednesday evening in Annapolis. Concentrating on sailing helped me keep everything else in the right perspective. The race would start at 6:00 PM and would be over in an hour or two, depending on how strong the wind was blowing. We would bring the boat in and have dinner consisting of some sandwiches and chips.

One evening, there was very little wind, and we were late finishing. I was feeling tired and unusually anxious as we ate dinner together. While driving out of Annapolis, I saw replicas of two of the ships Christopher Columbus sailed when he discovered America and it caused my anxiety to increase, like a feeling of dread, and I could not figure out why.[*] Then it was the dark outline of the trees along the edge highway that caused my anxiety to continue to increase. Finally, the aura started as a wave of nausea flowed down my chest and into my stomach.

I debated on whether to pull the car over or not. Usually the aura would soon go away. But this time it lingered and started to increase in intensity. There was a car on the side of the road and someone taking a tire off it, so I pulled up several yards behind them and put my car in park, then caught a glimpse of the clock. That was the last thing I remembered over the next fifteen minutes.

My car was running the whole time, and the person thought I was working on something in my car. When I could see again, they were done and approached me. I waved to them, hoping they would come help, and would have called out, but I could not speak. Apparently, they thought my wave was an indication of my not needing any assistance, so they turned around, walked back to their car, and drove away.

I couldn't see clearly and for several more minutes and wondered why everything was blurry. I thought the seizure was continuing as my vision would be focused for a moment then go blurry again. It took several more minutes for me to remember about my contact lenses and to realize the one in my dominant eye had fallen out during the seizure. The reason for the change in focus was due to my brain switching back and forth trying to determine which eye was dominate.

As my senses returned, my tongue hurt, I discovered saliva and blood on my shirt. Covering my dominant eye enabled me to see well enough to drive. The highway seemed very unfamiliar and I could not remember how to get home, even though I'd travelled this route many times before. Soon there was an exit ramp that looked familiar, and it took me onto the beltway around Baltimore. This was the proper exit, but not being sure that it was, I got off at the next exit, and was becoming totally lost.[†]

After driving for a while, I realized the need to turn around and get back on the beltway. I managed to make a U-turn and was having trouble finding the access ramp onto the beltway. My never having been in this area exacerbated the problem, and my vision was blurred to the point that reading signage was impossible. Then there were some green signs associated with the highway and suddenly, there was a ramp that brought me back on the beltway, and fortunately in the right direction. Twenty minutes later, as my memory was coming back, the route to get home became easy to apply.

I arrived home over an hour later than usual. Becky was awake and wondering where I'd been. I told her about the seizure and how it made me scared and extremely tired. After changing my clothes, I fell into bed. My head throbbed, and it would be a while before I fell asleep, even though my body was exhausted. The next day I informed the owner of the sailboat that crewing for them was no longer possible, and I felt saddened and defeated.

---

[*] Seeing certain types of settings may trigger feelings of de ja vu or of unknown doom in people with epilepsy and are now known as a focal or partial seizure.

[†] This was years before cell phones and contacting someone was impossible. Even if a phone was located, I could not remember my wife's name, phone number, or the fact the information was in my wallet.

Working for a general contractor had been too stressing and was taxing my body and brain. Now with a child, losing my job would have much more impact on the family. Becky and I were working in the fields of real estate and construction and if the economy were to decline would be unemployed at the same time. We agreed that it would be best for me to return to civil service and work for the Army Corps of Engineers. The next day I called the Army human resources department and learned they were still interested in hiring me. It brought a lot of relief to all of us.

Two years later, we had our second child—Steven. Steve was much more laid back and seemed to rely on Wes. As they grew older, I would hear Steve ask Wesley about my seizures. Steve seemed less intense, yet just as concerned.

Dr. Johnson was very good at helping me maintain control of my seizures. It seemed whenever I had a breakthrough seizure, a new medication would be approved to use as my secondary medication. He referred to me as the "Jaguar [car] that we have to keep finely tuned or the car [my brain] stops working."

Children, Driving, and Seizures

I refused to be isolated and stayed active with my children. Both liked to play sports, so I coached soccer and baseball teams when they were five to ten years old. It was a lot of fun being with all the children and their families on the teams. It became a lesson about leadership through the need to associate with the children at their level. It was an opportunity to teach about overcoming fear. Steve set a good example on what an influence this can have throughout a child's life as we worked to overcome his being afraid on the soccer field of people who were bigger than him.

Steven was five and had just started to play soccer. He would give the ball away to the children who were bigger than him no matter what team they were on. There was one child on another team who was a head taller and twenty pounds heavier than most of the other children. Everyone would give the ball to this child because they feared what he would do to them if they didn't.

One morning, we were in the kitchen and talked to Steve about why he would pass the ball to this boy. He told me that he feared what bigger people could do to him, so we talked of the advantages smaller people had over big people. Being five foot four myself, I explained our advantage was being closer to the ground and becoming tripping hazards to big people. He didn't believe me until we did a little drill. He ran at me as I dramatically ran toward him. When he hit my legs, I went over the top of him and crashed to the floor. He quickly turned around, and his mouth dropped open in disbelief. So, we did it again. He learned how to be the intimidator by screaming as he goes for the ball. We practiced many more times in the kitchen, laughing each time I wound up on the floor as he scurried away with the ball.

In the next game, the big kid had the ball and was coming down the field. Suddenly, Steve came running as fast as he could across the field and, as approached the ball, let loose with a loud shriek. The big kid looked up, then stopped as he saw Steve coming at him, then Steve tore the ball away from him and ran back up the field. He never gave the ball up again. The whole team did much better that year and several other children began to copy Steve. Even three years later Steve he had to be told by another coach not to scream anymore as he came after the ball.

Steve and Wes got into scouting, and there were various parent leadership positions for me to volunteer in and new friends to be made along the way. I was feeling good and doing well at home and at work. The best part was having confidence my seizures were under control with the support of Dr. Johnson and the new medications that were becoming available. But every time there was a seizure there was more damage to my brain and eventually the breakthrough seizures took their toll.

It was the summer of 2004 when the troop needed a scoutmaster for a week at summer camp with the younger boys. Wes was thirteen and Steve was ten, for Steve, it was his first time going to summer camp with the scouts. The week went well, but my sleep and eating habits were severely disrupted. The food that was available which was served at the dining facility wasn't the best for me. For one thing, cleanliness was much different than at home and it was not unusual to have some stomach issues develop. On some evenings, we ate at our campsite where the boys prepared the food.

Sleep was limited because I had to attend leadership meetings after the boys went to bed and then having to be the first person up in the morning. The leadership meetings were to review the schedules for the next day and share experience with other scoutmasters. I was the first one up in the morning, getting less than five hours sleep per night. They always say, "To be a scoutmaster takes one hour a week." (I would joke with friends of how the fine print said, "one hour per week per boy.") To keep going, my system was running on adrenalin and I was being physically stressed out. There was a significant change in my eating and sleep habits, stress and the environment, resulting in breaking four of the neurologist's rules. A seizure was coming.

On the morning of our last day, I overslept and was awakened by an aura. It did not seem bad, and I walked by myself to the bathroom, a quarter mile away. While there, I had another slightly more intense aura. The aura consisted of a wave of nausea that started slowly and intensified over the next few minutes and I could feel and hear my heart race. When looking in the mirror, I noticed my face was very pale. Fortunately, there was no loss consciousness. A high level of anxiety prevailed upon me and would not go away.

Later in the morning, we were packing up our equipment and checking out with the camp administration. The boys had done extremely well, and I was proud of all of them. By late morning, everything was ready, and two of the parents arrived to take a group back to the church that sponsored the troop. There the boys would put the equipment away and their parents would meet them. I should have been able to let myself calm down because I no longer had to be responsible for all nine boys, yet the anxiety persisted. All we had to do was make the stop at the church, then home.

Although there were people who could help me, I did not want to be a bother. I had taken responsibility for their children all week, and we were so close to everything coming to closure.

Driving home should not be a problem because the auras had diminished soon after I took my morning dose of medication. While driving on the way to the church, however, an aura occurred. This one wasn't nearly as bad as the last, so I kept going, although my anxiety level increased significantly. After arriving at the church, the boys unloaded the truck, and everyone returned to their families. Wes, Steve, and I were the last to leave, but that high level of anxiety prevailed. By this time, I had had several auras, some pretty intense, but thought my medication was very effective in preventing me from losing consciousness. We were only ten minutes from home now, and I felt that since we made it this far, we should be able to make it. We headed for home.

The next aura came when we were less than a mile and a half away from the house; this one was much more intense than the others. We were less than two minutes from home and thought we would be able to get there before the seizure went critical, if it did at all. We were now within a mile from home as we came through the entrance to the community; that's when I lost consciousness, and my foot went down on the gas pedal.

Wes had known something was wrong with me even though I had not said anything. He rode in the front passenger seat, and the moment I started to lose control, he was prepared. He took off his seat belt and climbed over the center console of our Chevy Avalanche while trying to keep control of the steering wheel. The truck went speeding down the hill and hit the curb several times. Steve was in the back seat and witnessed all of it.

About thirty seconds later, I regained some consciousness and was very confused. My vision was impaired, and I was looking down toward my feet. I had no sense of touch and could not feel anything through my hands and feet but was relieved to see my foot on the brake and the truck stopped. Suddenly, I saw a third foot near the driver's door. Who's could this be? Why was there another boot on the floor? As my peripheral vision started to return, the boots by the door and near the gas pedal was the same style and size. It would take a few more minutes before my peripheral vision recovered enough to comprehend that the leg attached to the third boot on the brake went up to my right. Wes came into view when I looked up that way. It was his boot pressing on the brake pedal. We were now less than a tenth of a mile from home.

Being so close to home, I told Wes to step off the brake so I could drive the rest of the way. He was upset and asked if this was a smart thing to do. I assured him it was and was able to turn left onto our street and drive the few hundred yards to our house. He sat beside me and kept his hand on the wheel. We pulled into the driveway and came to a stop right in front of the garage.

Becky was at the house and came outside to greet us. She saw the paleness of my face and immediately knew something was wrong. Answering her questions was impossible because part of my speech was impaired by the seizure. Wes told her what happened as I went inside the house and slept for several hours. It would take me several days to fully recover. My body hurt, and my tongue was sore from chewing on it. I fell into depression, amplified by the realization of the impact my seizures were having on our children.

A few days later, while going to work, I saw the tire marks from my truck on the curb. We hit the curb five times. Had Wes not been able to knock my foot off the gas pedal and get enough pressure on the brake to bring us to a stop, we would have plowed into some very large trees at the end of the road, one block from where we stopped. In his position, while struggling to get control of the truck, there was nothing that would have kept him from flying out the windshield, if we hit a tree. I kept thinking about how close Wes came close to becoming seriously injured or killed. It was a wake-up call about my failure to acknowledge the impact my seizures were having on my family and other people. I felt riddled with guilt and a sense of despair. There was no one available that could understand my battle with seizures and be able to provide appropriate assistance.

I had many auras throughout this time, and they were coming more often. Little did I know that with each seizure, more and more damage was being done to my brain. A year later we would learn that most of my left hippocampus was damaged and had shut down, except for the firestorms of the seizures that kept occurring in that area.

Breaking the Travel Rule

It was the spring of 2005, nearly a year after my seizure while driving with the boys, when we made a trip to visit friends and my Becky's aunt in California. On the second day, we were at her aunt's farm; I did not feel well and had no energy. It was a Sunday morning, and we went to church—an outdoor facility with lots of people. The anxiety attacks started as we were introduced to others. Meeting people never bothered me, but this time it made me feel uncomfortable, especially being around so many people. Responding to people as we were introduced was difficult to impossible for me as my speech was impaired. It seemed my brain was acting in slow motion and even finding some basic words to say was impossible.

When we returned to the farm, I let everyone know I was not feeling well and went to bed. Sleep came quickly and lasted for a couple of hours. When I woke up, my tongue and the side of my mouth hurt from my chewing on them, the consequence of a seizure that occurred during my sleep. I felt exhausted yet obligated to be social, so I joined everyone for lunch. Eating was difficult because of the injury to my mouth, but I couldn't tell any about the seizure because of the poor health of the grandmother and not wanting to alarm her. Everyone was excited about being on the farm, and the boys, Becky, and her aunt and uncle went outside. I was sitting on the couch with my wife's 102-year-old grandmother sitting near me.

I was drifting in and out of sleep when the aura came and rapidly intensified; a wave of nausea and high anxiety caused my body to tremble and my heart rate to increase significantly. The seizure quickly intensified, and my body went rigid and shook. For a moment I could see nothing but darkness as the seizure raged in my brain. Part of me was screaming for control while another part was cut off, in total darkness. Then my vision would flash on for a second and then cut off—back to the darkness and the void. When my vision was effective, I could see the grandmother (who was nearly blind) getting upset as she sensed something bad was happening to me. She was shouting for help [I could not hear her], and there was no one there to help. Her blindness prevented her from getting up and finding someone.

My body would go rigid for several seconds, then relax. My breathing was erratic. The uncle, who was just outside the house, heard the grandmother and came running into the room. When he realized what was happening, he went to his closet and grabbed his shotgun, which he kept handy to protect the animals on the farm. He ran outside and fired several times in the air to get Becky's attention. She and the boys were out riding in a field on an all-wheel drive vehicle. When she heard the gunfire they immediately headed to the house. The seizure still had control as she came into the room. She asked me some questions, but I was ~~none responsive~~nonresponsive. Then I heard her say to her uncle, "Call 911." As the seizure subsided and my vision returned, I could see my children in the room but keeping a distance from me. They had expressions of fear and deep sadness in their eyes.

My body turned blue from interrupted breathing, and I could not talk. My right leg hurt from having it under the couch where it could not go straight when the muscles seized. Some muscle in my thigh had been stretched and torn; there was a lot of pain. When the paramedics arrived, I was given oxygen, and started to recover. The blue tint of my flesh quickly faded, and my color came back, although I was pale from exhaustion.

Transportation to the hospital was deemed necessary for blood test and observation. I needed to get to the bathroom, and although my speech was impeded, was able to communicate by pointing to the bathroom and moving my head when asked if I needed to go. Assistance was provided to help me walk and some privacy given with the door partially opened, so the paramedics could respond if I fell. The gurney had been transformed into a chair so I could be carried down the steep turning staircase. This was necessary because of the injury to my leg and my inability to comprehend how to go down the steps. On the way to the hospital, a paramedic asked me numerous times, "What is your name?" and "Where are you now?" I could not answer him until shortly before getting to the hospital, nearly thirty minutes later and an hour since the seizure. Even then all I could say was "Jon" and "I am in an ambulance."

I felt like I'd been in a major fight and lost. My head ached and my body was exhausted and hurt, not only in the leg but throughout. My tongue had been clamped between my teeth, and the walls of my mouth had been chewed on. It hurt to walk and took effort to move my arms. At the hospital, blood tests were immediately performed, and the results indicated my medication level was very low. I had been taking my medication as scheduled; however, something with the travel to California and possibly having a twenty-four-hour flu impacted how fast it was metabolized.

We slept at our hotel that night while the boys stayed with Becky's aunt and uncle. They were to stay with us at the hotel; however, we figured they would not sleep well being worried about their dad, especially if I had another seizure. There was much concern about my wife's grandmother and what she witnessed. Overall, I felt like crap—physically and emotionally—from my seizure and what people had to see. Although I was very concerned about everyone, I fell asleep because my body and mind were too exhausted.

The next day, we returned to the farm to be with the boys. Wes did not appear to have slept much as indicated by the dark rings under his eyes. He told me how worried he was about losing me. What he saw prior to the paramedics arriving had him thinking I was going to die, and there was nothing he could do about it. Steven was trying to understand everything that happened. He hadn't slept well either. The grandmother was pleased we were back, and we talked about what the seizure was like for both of us. I told her that I saw her yelling for help while having the seizure and feeling bad about what she had witnessed. She assured me that everything would be okay and reminded me about the importance of taking care of myself. She then told me we were going to have a birthday celebration; I did not remember it was my forty-sixth birthday. This was the year epilepsy seized control of my entire life.

No More Medications Available

It was the spring of 2005; something was happening within me and my ability to live with seizures was diminishing. I had been on numerous medications and combinations thereof. Some had severe impact to my personality; others worked fine for a couple of years, then they stopped being effective as the seizures broke through the protective boundary the medication created. It made me very nervous to refer to my neurologist because I feared there were no new medications available to control my seizures, that would mean the seizures had won. I called him when we returned from California to talk about what happened and what he thought needed to be done.

Once again, he told me there was a new medication called Lamictal that could be very effective for me. Due to the potential of the side effects, I was to see him within six weeks for a follow up. When the follow-up appointment came, there were numerous cold sores in my mouth and he directed me to immediately stop taking the medication, because such reactions were an indicator the it may be doing serious damage to my body's organs. Phenobarbital was then prescribed, which caused me to slip into a deep sleep. I was not able to stay fully awake and became nonfunctional, zombie like. Now I had run out of options for medications available to treat my seizures. I was directed to stay on the Dilantin through the summer, the season when my seizures were least likely to occur, and to hope something new would come along soon.

More Seizures and Depression

As the fall season came, the daylight time became shorter, and the stress associated with the boys' school and work my work obligations made me more susceptible to breakthrough seizures. This brought on one to two simple partial seizures a week. After being on so many different medications and having the breakthrough seizures, they were now considered to be intractable, untreatable. My brain was damaged to the extent that even low-level stress and minor changes to diet and sleep triggered seizures. My neurologist informed me that more extensive care was required as the epilepsy spun out of control. It was time to return to Johns Hopkins Hospital.

I slipped into a state of depression that lasted several weeks. Nothing seemed to be going right. Everything I owned and cared for was lost as my seizures became intractable. Drug reactions effected my memory and mood. Rejection by others was my greatest fear, enhanced by the limitations with transportation and becoming dependent on other people. It felt like I was being a burden while not being able to give anything back. Sometimes it felt like having a gun to my head that someday would go off.

Some relief came over me while taking our golden retriever for a walk, but when we returned home I was enveloped by the thought of dying.* Was this caused by the depression associated with epilepsy or a side effect of the high dose of medication required in an attempt to control my seizures? I did not know. All I knew was it was happening regularly, and it was staying with me for longer periods of time.

I relied on a strong faith which was being tested. It must have been God telling me years before while windsurfing, "I have plans for you." However, if such plans really existed, what were they? I had been the project manager on the construction of a national monument dedicated to the Korean War veterans, which required all my knowledge and skills. It was extremely

---

* Years later, while studying psychotherapy, I learned about suicidal premonitions/ideations. This is a time when someone has thoughts about suicide without a plan in place to carry it out.

challenging, but the project touched thousands, so that must have been the part of the plan. My twenty-year contract with God was up, too, yet I was still alive. There must be more than this, because my boys were in high school and middle school, and I needed to be available for them.

Section 4
Professional Career

Chapter 5
The Navy (1981–1989)

The only thing you will ever be allowed to do is to sit at a desk and sharpen pencils

My career as an engineer started soon after graduating with the US Navy at the Shipyard in Charleston, South Carolina. It made me feel good about being able to serve my country, especially with the Navy. My father was the engineer on a ship in WWII and was recalled during the Korean War so there was a lot of family pride in what I was doing. At the age of twenty-two, I wanted to make him proud of me. This was also a time when the Cold War with the Soviet Union intensified as Ronald Reagan had just become president and wanted to rebuild the military. Over the next seven years the Navy would double in size and have the appropriate facilities to make it strong.

Medical Review

On my first day of work, there were two major events in my life that took place. The first involved a physical that was required prior to coming on the shipyard; the other was meeting another person diagnosed with epilepsy. The first event nearly destroyed my career; the second led to a great friendship.

Before reporting to work, there was a medical clinic just outside the shipyard where new employees were to have a physical. This was required to determine if the person could operate or even be near the equipment necessary to work on the ships and submarines being overhauled at the shipyard. The outcome nearly caused me to quit before even getting to the office where I was assigned to work.

The morning started with me going through an extensive physical. This enabled the Navy to establish a person's physical condition. It entailed hearing and vision tests, breathing tests, review of family history, addictive behaviors, and testing for exposure to lead and asbestos. These concluded with a physical with a doctor who reviewed the information from the test completed earlier in the day. Upon completing this review, the doctor discussed personal history with the employee and then did a physical involving the basics of listening to your breathing, checking blood pressure, and a hernia check.

Based on the outcome, a determination was made concerning the person's capability of performing various tasks associated with the area of work they were assigned. Essentially, they wanted to determine if a person had a physical condition that would make them a risk to themselves and others or be a liability to the government in the future. This was very important when being near or operating various machinery or being inside the components of a ship or submarine where the space can be limited and very tight.

The physical was an interesting process that took nearly a day to go through, most of the time was spent waiting in line for the next test. It seemed quite a few people were hired at the same time with a day each month assigned to the medical staff to focus on the physicals. Local doctors aided with expediting the process. There was the standard vision and hearing test, evaluating your height and weight, checking your feet, and testing to make sure your lungs weren't already damaged from smoking or other form of toxic exposure. These were the days where employers were beginning to be held responsible for damages and injuries to employees exposed to asbestos and lead.

They also reviewed the health history provided by the individual. The last step was filling out the documents required to obtain a security clearance to enable you to enter the shipyard. The level of security clearance depended on your area of work and obtaining additional information and a formal security review. If you made it through all this, you were issued work boots and safety glasses and reported to your supervisor.

The Freak

I did well with all the tests, all the way up to the point of meeting with the doctor and getting his certification. While sitting on the exam table, the doctor read the information concerning the outcome of the tests and the questionnaire I completed concerning my medical history. Due to the arrangement of the room, the doctor's desk was mounted to the wall, and his back was turned to me. A few minutes into his review, he suddenly stood straight and said, "Looky here, I've got me a goddamn freak." I couldn't believe what I heard, with his back turned to me, so I asked him to repeat himself.

This time he turned around to look me straight in the eyes and said, "You've got epilepsy, and that makes you a goddamned freak. The only thing you will be allowed to do working in this shipyard is to sit behind a desk and sharpen pencils. We don't allow freaks to work here."

The doctor could not use my epilepsy to prevent me from coming to work for the federal government, but it seemed he had the power to make sure I didn't enjoy it. He was trying to discourage me from ever wanting to work at the shipyard. He completed the physical, of which I had no problem, because of being in very good physical shape, except for the seizures. The only exception was feeling broken inside after being called "a goddamned freak."* As I left the building, the staff provided guidance on the location of the Production Engineering Office where I was assigned to work.

Should I Quit?

After walking out of the building, I stopped and gave serious consideration to walking away from the shipyard and getting into my car to drive away. Then I thought it best to go meet with my assigned supervisor and tell him I would not be working at the shipyard. In the fifteen minutes it took to walk to the office, I thought about what to say about quitting. The

---

* Nearly forty-years later there is still a large contingent of people in the USA that consider people with epilepsy to be freaks. Most of this comes from the ignorance of seizure disorders amongst the population, the assumptions by church organizations based on scripture, and emergency medical services and staff assuming seizures are caused by drug and alcohol addictions.

discouragement led to thinking about heading back to my parents' house on Long Island and what their reaction would be, especially my dad's.

There was no need to introduce myself while entering my supervisor's office. I immediately said, "I have been told by the doctor I cannot work here, so I plan on leaving. I wish I had known this before. I would never have bothered to come." There was no way I would just sit behind a desk all day and not be allowed to oversee the work being accomplished. My supervisor, who had not even had the opportunity to get up from his desk to introduce himself, surprised me by smiling and saying, "according to me, what happened in the doctor's office has no impact on your working for me or having access to the shipyard."

What he said was about to turn the situation into one of the greatest days of my life. Instead of encouraging me to leave as the doctor implied, the supervisor explained how the doctor had no authority over my work in the shipyard. The supervisor was responsible in assigning the work and for my safety. Most importantly he told me about another person working for him who had epilepsy. He called Mark Leyde into his office before we started talking about the job and responsibilities of his team. Mark was considerably bigger than me (six feet) and very warmhearted as he smiled and shook my hand, welcoming me on board. The supervisor told Mark that the two of us had much in common, even though we had never met each other. Mark looked at me with a questioning expression, trying to figure out what he could have in common with someone he'd never met before. Then he was told, "Jon has epilepsy too." Mark smiled and shook my hand again, this time with both hands, and he did not seem to want to let go. He let me know that if I needed anything to please come and see him. We soon got together after work and started sharing our experiences with each other, the impact of living with seizures, and our love of the water.

Mark

Mark invited me out to the house he rented from our supervisor on the Isle of Palms, just two blocks from the ocean and four blocks from a boat ramp to the Intracoastal Waterway. He shared the house with several interns from the University of Tennessee who worked in our section. It was a nice cinderblock house that held up well to the wear and tear of a bunch of young engineers. Our supervisor appreciated the renovations and upgrade work we did for him. We could be open with each other about our experiences dealing with seizures, the impact it had on getting through engineering school, and associating with other people. It was nice to have someone who could associate with what it is like to have a seizure and the effect it has on the mind and body. After just a few days, Mark said, "I feel like I have known you all of my life." We became best of friends.

Nuclear Submarines

At work, I could now do more than just sharpen pencils as my seizures were controlled with medication, with little side effects to my mental abilities. Mark knew which neurologist to see and what to say about having a seizure that would not lead to the loss of a driver's license.

Back at that time treatment was relatively simple. Just a few medications were available and not much monitoring on the blood levels. My friendship with Mark continued until his death in 2014 from a car accident; for some reason he lost consciousness and crossed the double line into oncoming traffic.

My supervisor gave me a tour through the dry docks where nuclear-driven fast-attack submarines were being overhauled and refueled. It was amazing to see how a submarine was brought into a dry dock—the water pumped out, and the submarine settled on a series of concrete blocks that would provide support in the appropriate place and keep it structurally sound. The blocks would also keep it from rolling over and created a tunnel to the underside of the boat. Whole sections of the hull were removed to allow access to the reactors and engine rooms.

The submarines are amazing in that they can go for months without surfacing. This is due to their power source being a nuclear reactor. While in dry dock, the reactor would be deactivated. This brought the temperatures down, yet it still required a certain level of cooling and close monitoring. There were piping systems and several backup systems in place to make sure cooling was not interrupted and to keep it safe. Exposure to radiation was closely monitored and with all the protective barriers and systems most workers were exposed to less radiation than the public was through natural exposure to the sun during the day.

I learned about the various trades involved in performing the work and the criteria and regulations applied to make sure the systems were kept operational. Although all this was fascinating, it didn't seem to apply to me and my desire to move into the field of construction. Six months later, I transferred to the Southern Division, Naval Facilities Engineering Command (known at the time as SOUTHDIV NAVFAC) Construction Division field office at the naval base.

It was a great opportunity for me as a civil engineer, because funding was being provided to upgrade and increase the size of the Navy at the height of the Cold War. The experience of working in the shipyard helped with managing the construction projects later assigned to me that effected shipyard operations. My seizures were controlled with medication, and there was someone who could associate with me on what it was like living with epilepsy.

Waterfront

The work with SOUTHDIV was at the field office at the Charleston Naval Base and operated by the resident engineer (civilian) and the resident officer (a Navy commander). The staff consisted of a civilian group to maintain continuity and Navy officers for coordination with the Navy customers. I was in training and worked for another project manager and the inspection staff who taught me more about construction than could have ever been learned in a classroom. They worked with me when I had my seizure and helped me build a strong level of confidence and self-esteem.

Over the first two years, I was assigned to work under a project manager who had nearly thirty years of experience overseeing construction contracts. He taught me how to maintain working relationships with the team and the importance of completing the contracts in a manner that made the contractors, customers, and the government winners. The inspectors were mostly retired construction supervisors, so they knew what to look for and made sure the quality of the work met or exceeded the contract requirements and customer expectations. I spent many hours in the field with them learning about the techniques and quality of construction. When asked about my experience levels by customers, my response was "I just have a couple of years of field experience. However, I have access to a team of project managers and inspectors with over three hundred years' experience to support me."

The projects assigned to me started with the smaller renovation and upgrade to buildings. As I learned through other people's experience and demonstrated my ability to manage projects, I was given more complex contracts. Due to the onslaught of projects and lack of staff, several projects that involved waterfront and pier renovations were assigned to me, that would impact naval operations. The renovations required sections of a pier to be shut down to enable the contractors to access to the utilities; steam, water, sewer, and electrical systems being upgraded. These utilities are necessary for ships to operate and are generated by the ship while underway.

Beck's navy friends who were serving on some of the ships had made me aware that without shore power and utilities, part of the crew had to stay on board while in port to maintain the ship's systems. Leave was very important, especially to those who had been deployed for several months to over a year. Many just wanted to go home and be with their families.

Over the next several months Congress had approved millions of dollars of construction funding to enable the Navy to upgrade nearly all their facilities at the base and several more contracts were awarded requiring upgrades to all the piers. The outages required on the utilities and simultaneously shutting down operations on several piers at a time would impact nearly all ship operations. The more I learned about all the contracts and my ability to understand the impact they would have to ship operations lead me to my supervisor's office. There were two piers that were to be torn down and replaced; one new prototype pier was to be constructed and structural improvements and utility upgrades on twenty other piers. My estimate was that thirty to sixty percent of the areas used to dock the cruisers, destroyers, submarines, and other support craft would be out of service for nearly three years. When I talked to my supervisor about this, he had me put together a presentation package to raise our concern to those who would be affected.

A meeting was scheduled with the junior officers from SOUTHDIV, the Charleston Naval Shipyard Department of Public Works, and Naval Station Ship Operations, along with the officers of several ships. After presenting the information, everyone said this had to go up to their chain of command. Within a week, I was doing the same presentation to the station supervisors and Navy commanders. They all agreed this was a serious issue, and another meeting was scheduled with next level of command, which comprised of the captains and the commanders involved at the shipyard and the chiefs at SOUTHDIV. We were to meet at SOUTHDIV headquarters a few miles from the naval base.

I was two and a half years out of college, delivering the message about coordinating the work with ships operations to those in the highest positions at the naval base, and several of the captains of the destroyers and cruisers stationed at Charleston. The civilians were dressed in suits and ties and the captains in summer white uniforms. Having no knowledge of who these people were or the level of their authority, was an advantage because my ignorance prevented me from being nervous about presenting the issues. Standing in front of the room doing the presentation with a diagram of the piers with the utility outages highlighted and timelines of the work schedule seemed easier because of having already done it twice. The issue was eight to ten of the station's piers, roughly a third, would have to be shut down simultaneously to meet the schedule criteria in the contracts.

After completing the presentation, one of the civilian division chiefs said, "Seems like all the ships will have to go to sea for a while." The room went dead silent as nobody could believe what was just said. It was like I was waiting to be shot. His statement made it seem this was very close to this happening.

Then the captain of one of the cruisers slowly stood up and said, "You seem to have forgotten who you are here to support. I am letting you know this building is within range of the guns on my ship." He picked up his hat and walked brusquely out of the room. The uneasy silence continued for several more minutes, and I felt like the end was near. Finally, the chief of the construction division looked at me and said, "Looks like you have a lot of projects to coordinate. Make sure you do so with minimal impact to the ships."

The three-year program took nearly four and a half years, to complete. I was assigned as the assistant resident engineer or construction manager on the renovation of utilities and structural repairs to nineteen piers, replacement of two piers, and the construction of a prototype double-deck pier, Pier Zulu, which became a Navy standard. There was a lot of help and support that was provided to me along the way while coordinating the schedules with the Navy Operations Division and the general contractors. I was able to get acquainted with just about everyone dealing with ship operations and public works along the waterfront and the contractor's appreciated the support in getting the work completed.

In our office, we had a lieutenant come on board to oversee some of the building facility contracts. He had been an F-14 fighter pilot who developed a vision issue that prevented him from flying fighter jets. We became friends, and he offered to take me up in a Cessna 150 to get photos of the waterfront work. The security officer gave us permission to fly over the restricted area of the naval base. The Department of Public Works (DPW) requested more photos and gave us a list of projects to photograph. When we were officially given the security clearance, we obtained two cameras and several rolls of film and headed for the plane.

We took off from the Isle of Palms, about twenty miles away from the base, and enjoyed seeing the coastline from a couple thousand feet. The first project we were to photograph was Pier Zulu, the new prototype pier that was 70 percent complete. As we approached the naval base, I heard on the radio calls to the security office from several ships. They were very concerned about a Cessna 150 approaching the piers. There was no response from security. This went on for several minutes, and by this time, we had the nose of the plane down and were getting great photos of the construction of the pier. We were so tied up in the approach and taking photos that we weren't paying attention to the radio calls. They got our attention when we heard "Request permission to open fire" from one of the ships. Realizing that we were the plane in question just about took my breath away. A moment later we heard "DO NOT FIRE! DO NOT FIRE!" "SADLER'S IN THAT PLANE!" "THAT PLANE HAS PERMISSION TO FLY OVER." At this point, we had flown so low I could see the work crew in the electrical vault on the pier and the lights on the 150-foot light poles directly across from me as the plane was pulling up. The lieutenant was calm about the situation and told me how he could have landed the plane with the engine stopped and the wings shot off. He assured me we would be alive; he just couldn't guarantee what we would look like. He then asked, "Should we do it again?" And I said, "Sure," and started to change the film in the cameras.

My supervisor was terrific at keeping peace with the upper command of the agencies involved in the work. He motivated me and provided guidance and suggestions at the appropriate time. Some of the most interesting parts of my role involved negotiating change orders and developing the revisions to the design necessary when unforeseen conditions were discovered. I was negotiating and documenting changes of over $1.5 million as valued in 1985, supported by a well-experienced team of people from the field staff, and headquarters, along with the customers.

As the work was completed along the waterfront, a new pier was to be constructed at the Naval Weapons Station, located upriver from the naval base, for a special training facility. As part of the Cold War, the United States and the Soviet Union agreed to decrease the number of ballistic submarines capable of carrying nuclear warheads. One of these would be turned into a training facility for the officers and crew responsible in maintaining the nuclear reactors on submarines and warships. The ballistic missile submarine was taken into the shipyard and had the midsection, where the missile tubes were located, removed. It was welded back together and made fully operational. The pier had to be completed in time to provide anchorage for the submarine and slips for the support vessels when they were ready. I moved to the weapons station to oversee the work.

At the time, I did not know my son would be stationed there to complete his training to become qualified as an officer overseeing the nuclear reactors on the most sophisticated aircraft carriers of his time. As he told me about the facility, I kept saying, "I know." Finally, he asked me how I knew so much, and let me share my experience. It just seemed amazing that I could be part of all of it, especially after what the doctor had said about my epilepsy and only ever "being allowed to sharpen pencils."

The only way this became possible was through the doctors who provided appropriate medical care and treatment and my supervisor who recognized my abilities to manage and lead. The opportunities this created helped me to fulfill the task of even higher positions than I ever dreamed possible.

Philadelphia Shipyard

My career with the Navy continued for another year and a half as we moved to Philadelphia, Pennsylvania, so Becky could pursue a graduate degree. The Philadelphia shipyard had deeper water than Charleston which allowed it to accommodate aircraft carriers. The

Northern Division of the Naval Facilities Engineering Command (NORTHDIV) headquarters was stationed there. We lived in downtown Philadelphia, close to where Becky was going to graduate school. Living in downtown Philadelphia contributed to more stress, exacerbated by long periods of driving that was needed to get to work. There was no public transportation that could accommodate my needs, and unlike Charleston, I now had to drive by myself.

The new job involved developing the design of facilities to support the families and facilities away from the waterfront. The first assignment was to become a paving specialist working on runway systems. This required my going back to college and studying highway and paving design. This was a good challenge to keep my brain working hard. As Becky completed her degree, we decided Philadelphia was not for us and moved to Baltimore, Maryland. In Baltimore, there would be numerous opportunities for both our careers and fortunately, the most advanced medical care for people living with epilepsy.

Chapter 6
General Construction Contractor (1989–1991)

The hell you will. If I had five of him, I'd fire the rest of you

When Becky completed graduate school, we looked for employment in the Baltimore region. I had interviewed with the Navy in Washington, DC; the Army Corps of Engineers and a general contractor in Baltimore. The position fell through with the Navy, and there was a hiring freeze with the Corps. Wanting to be with my wife and getting another perspective of construction, I accepted the project engineer position with the contractor. The phone call from the Army Corps of Engineers came the day I was packing my belongings and leaving the Navy. The position was now available, and they wanted to talk about my start date. I thanked and informed them they were a little late with the formal offer.

Working for a general contractor was more stressful, because the hours required to assemble a contract proposal and providing reports to customers often required working overtime and impacted my sleep and eating. The stress levels increased with the worries of delivering products on time. Within a few months, our first child, Wesley, was born. And the struggle of being a father and the devotion to the employer increased my stress considerably. All these physical and emotional stressors led to breakthrough seizures.

At work, my supervisor gave me a special assignment to develop a computer program for tracking budgets and costs on a multimillion-dollar project. Although the software existed to create a database of information on such items as cost and budget, the programs had to be written to produce the reports. My supervisor called me into his office and asked if such programs could be developed. Not knowing the schedule and level of importance, I assured him it could be done.

It was a challenge that often required working many hours into the early morning. Then there was home and the child to care for. My fellow employees would often joke about how sleep was an option we had to give up because of our responsibilities at home and work. For me, sleep was a necessity needed to control my seizures. With such stressors, the probability of my having a seizure increased significantly. It was only a matter of time.

Writing the programs seemed easy at first. Then the reports became more detailed, and data input had to be revised. The programs went from several hundreds to thousands of commands. Much time was required to troubleshoot the programs and database entries for typos as either caused the reports to be worthless. I was the only person who could provide training on the data entry and the importance of not making typographical errors. The invoices were based on the direct costs of a project, so everything from buying pencils to paying staff and subcontractors had to be entered. At the peak of a project, thousands of data entries were required per month.

Seizure Breakthroughs and Job Impact

The grand mal seizure happened while writing a new program to generate a report. It was very stressful, for the program had to be completed and the report available within a couple of days. There was a very important meeting with the customer, and the company wanted to make a good impression on how they were unique in tracking budgets and costs. The aura came while I was troubleshooting the program. Hoping it would just go away, I continued working, a few minutes later it suddenly intensified. There was no place to go and felt safe sitting in a chair in a small room by myself. The probability of someone noticing an aura happening was low.

The aura continued into the ictal stage of a general complex seizure (grand mal), and many people heard me banging against my chair and table. I have no memory of my muscle suddenly tightening and my body going straight as a board while sitting in the chair. I was chewing on my tongue, and blood was dripping out of my mouth and onto my white dress shirt. I then lost my peripheral vision and could only see the computer screen in front of me. Soon it seemed to drift away from me and disappear.

About fifteen minutes later I started to regain some consciousness and there was an associate standing next to me. She was talking to others and asking me questions. I was nonresponsive yet could hear and remember her telling an associate to "Call 911." She had a look of concern on her face and kept telling other people to stay out of the room. She did not understand what had happened and answered her colleagues that medical help was on the way. My vision was turning off and on with no peripheral vision. I was not able to move or respond; but could hear and comprehend what was being said around me. There was an ongoing battle occurring in my brain and I struggled with thoughts of the possibility of not recovering.

By the time the paramedics arrived, over thirty minutes since the aura started, my vision had returned to almost normal. But my speech was still impaired. They were asking me questions and trying to get a heart monitor on me. I was frustrated because there was no way to communicate with them. I gestured for a pen and thought, *if I cannot say anything, maybe I can write it.* This didn't work either. It was at this time the CEO came into the room. He saw me push the paramedics away and go back to the keyboard of the computer. I didn't want to lose all my work and remembered to type "save," and then shut it off.

I picked up the phone and dialed the number to Becky's office. I clearly asked the secretary, "Is Becky there?" The secretary said, "She is out of the office. How can I help you?" The only word I could find in my mind was *shit.* After saying this, I handed the phone to a paramedic. He explained to the secretary that I had had a seizure and they needed to talk to my wife immediately.

The secretary got so excited and scared about what was happening that she had one of the other employees in her office run out the door and speed off in his car to find Becky. Becky had to calm her staff down by telling them she knew of my condition and then called my office. She talked to the project manager I was working with and gave him the phone number and address of my neurologist. Since she was at the other side of Baltimore from the construction office, she asked if the company could provide transportation. She would meet us at the doctor's office.

Upon learning there was already professional care established for my condition, the paramedics agreed not to transport me to a hospital. My cognitive abilities had returned to the point of being able to sign with my initials the forms necessary for this to happen. My associate told me I looked like I had been in a street fight as he walked me out to his car to take me to the neurologist. This was not a very long walk and required riding in an elevator. Even so, it felt like his car was miles away as my body hurt and was exhausted.

Due to a traffic jam, the forty-five-minute ride to the neurologist's office took over two hours, and then another hour to see the doctor. By this time, I was fully cognitive and had been talking to my work associate about the details of what happened as he drove. From the doctor's perspective, they didn't see much concern with my having the seizure, except the blood on my shirt and the injury to my mouth and tongue. Any changes necessary with my medication would be determined based on the results of the blood test to check my medication level. They were very helpful with my associate and Becky's concerns as they informed them that my mouth would heal, and I would be okay. They gave me a note to give my supervisor as my medical excuse. With my supervisor and the CEO witnessing the aftermath of the seizure, the note was not necessary.

Within a few days, I learned how the CEO had called my supervisor to his office to talk about what happened. The supervisor was nervous and feared being reprimanded for hiring a person with epilepsy. As he walked into the CEO's office, he immediately started explaining how he planned to fire me the next day. The CEO cut him off as he said, "The hell you will, if I had five people as dedicated to this company as that young man, I could get rid of all of you." Seems he was very impressed with my pushing the paramedics away to save my computer work, especially in the physical and mental state I was in.

Job Stress

Working for a construction firm and wondering where the next dollar was coming from was very stressful which drastically increased in knowing my supervisor was wanting to fire me. I started having more breakthrough seizures several times a week, then almost every day. All of them were partial complex seizures that interrupted my ability to speak and process any work. My work associates knew what to do and would get up from their desk and close our office door when the seizure started. They continued with their work and talked to me when I became more cognitive. I could no longer drive and had to rely on another associate for transportation.

The computer programs were working well, and the supervisor notified me that my next assignment would be on a project located a few hundred miles away. This seemed impossible because of my not being able to drive. He gave me a good performance evaluation then reached in his wallet and gave me a couple of dollars for my effort, very unlike what was given the other employees. The message was received, it was time to leave.

That afternoon I contacted the Army Corps of Engineers to see if they were still interested in hiring me. Within an hour the director of the design management branch returned my call, he remembered me from my interview nearly three years earlier. He was excited that I was interested in working for the Corps. Within a couple of weeks, the position was officially offered, and I immediately accepted it. I gave the two-week notification of leaving the construction firm the next day. My job security, along with work hours, was much better than working for a construction contractor. The transportation issue was solved, as there was a subway near my home with stops near the office. The best part was that my stress level decreased to the point that the triggers to my seizures were reduced and the medication became very effective once more in controlling them.

I had worked for the general contractor for two years and learned more about their roles in completing projects and programs. Most importantly, I was learning how stress levels played a major role in triggering my seizures. While working with the Army Corps of Engineers, however, there would come a time when even higher levels of stress would occur and lead to my seizures becoming intractable once more.

Chapter 7
The Army Corps of Engineers (1991–2015)

Your future forecast of project management and removing the stovepipes in the
agency is already happening.

— An office associate

My work experience as a civil engineer and project manager with the Baltimore District (North Atlantic Baltimore or NAB) of the Army Corps of Engineers (USACE) thrust me into a leadership role. I started as a design manager, responsible for the administration of multimillion-dollar contracts with Architect-Engineering (design) firms. Some of the projects involved great detail and planning as they were associated with medical and biological research facilities. Within two years, the Programs and Project Management Division (PPMD) was developed for the oversight of entire projects and they were looking for volunteers to fill the positions. It was the perfect opportunity for me to apply my experience and become one of the district's project managers (PM) for the military programs. There was much to learn as the work involved the planning, design, and construction phases, then the turnover and follow-up with the agencies involved.

Soon after becoming a PM the 1995 Base Realignment and Closure Program was activated by Congress and required significant upgrades to the facilities at Fort Detrick, Maryland. The projects were intense, and the five-year program had to be completed in three years. Soon after this, came the Korean War Veterans Memorial in Washington, DC, that involved coordination between in-house staff, military agencies, Congress, and presidential appointees. Other programs would follow that required much effort and high levels of responsibility.

My experience of living with epilepsy facilitated the development of my leadership skills because I discovered working with people was much easier than having a seizure. My secret helped me to become aware that there is much more to the people on the teams than what could be seen with the naked eye. Demonstrating an interest in the team members and understanding the challenges they faced is what was needed to keep the projects moving forward.

My experience with the Navy and the general contractor gave me a good comprehension of the level of effort and demands required in each phase of a project. There were many opportunities to work on projects that were unique and demanding. For many years, I was able to control my seizures by managing my stress and taking care of myself. Eventually, the demands and stress of the projects wore away the effectiveness of the medications and my brains ability to control the triggers to a seizure.

The 1995 Base Realignment and Closure (BRAC)

The Base Realignment and Closure (BRAC) involved having new facilities constructed at Fort Detrick, MD for the agencies to relocate from Fort Ritchie, MD and several other facilities nationwide that were being closed. The need to complete a five-year program in three years increased my stress levels significantly. The standard manners of procurement and contract administration had to be set aside, allowing people to be more creative to achieve what seemed to be impossible. The District operated through a stovepipe management system of planning, engineering, and construction divisions. Each division would complete their part of the project, then passed it off to the next. Planning for the scope and funding requirements, Engineering for the design, and Construction for the construction of the facilities. When following this management system, it typically required five years to complete a project. To meet the BRAC schedule, the stovepipe system had to be set aside, and all three divisions had to interact and work close with each other, something that was very atypical.

Working with and coordinating the teams, consisting of a few to over a hundred people of various races, ethnicities, trades, and degrees, was necessary to bring together the final product, that met the needs of the military, and several other federal agencies. Completing the work ahead of schedule, and the feedback from my constituents played a tremendous role in rebuilding and boosting everyone's self-esteem.

Often on such large programs, the design would be contracted to an architectural and engineering firm, which required five to six months to award a contract and the work to start. There was no time to contract out the design of the projects, so it was completed by the in-house design branch staff. My role as a project manager went beyond working with the other managers, because the staff had to be motivated to work overtime for six to nine months, not just a few evenings or a couple of weeks. It was amazing to see how people were motivated by receiving some form of appreciation, be it a handshake, an update, or pictures of the project they had worked on.

There were various meetings that had to be attended outside of NAB that involved the higher-level management of many agencies to provide updates and coordinate the schedules for building occupancies. A couple of days a month, I rode in a van with the executive officer (XO), helping him prepare for briefings to the customers and high-level management from Washington, DC.* Having such transportation was a relief, because driving to and from these meetings brought about my greatest fear, that of having a seizure while on a major highway. The primary concern of everyone in the meetings was the construction schedule.

With six months left to complete the program, I attended a high-level meeting with the XO, who had to brief a two-star general responsible for the closure of Fort Ritchie on the status of the new work. When the general asked the XO if the construction would be completed in time for the personnel to relocate to Fort Detrick, the XO looked at me, and I nodded my head. His response to the general was "Yes, sir." On the ride back to NAB, the XO looked at me and asked for reassurance that the work would be done in time. Knowing the people of the teams involved

---

* The executive officer is the second-in-command—in this case, the second-in-command of the Baltimore District. There are five levels of those ranked as generals and are ranked from one star up to five stars depending on their level of responsibility.

and their motivation to complete the program, I assured him the work would be complete on or ahead of schedule.

Occasionally I would have a breakthrough seizure, but the seizures were minor, and most of the time these did not cause me to lose consciousness. I kept my neurologist informed of my seizures and was prescribed new medications when needed and as they became available. My neurologist kept me on Dilantin and used the new medications as a secondary treatment.

My stress level seemed to have decreased thanks to the devotion of the people working on the program. My working a few days a week at the construction sites and the remainder at NAB with the design team, enabled me to understand the needs of both and be assured any problems that came along were promptly and appropriately addressed. Meetings were scheduled and site visits arranged to obtain the information needed to keep the work moving smoothly. The schedule was met with three weeks to spare, and the move of personnel to Fort Detrick proceeded without a problem.

The Korean War Veterans Memorial (1994–1999)

As the BRAC work was completed, I was assigned to be the PM on the Korean War Veterans Memorial (KWVM). The memorial had reached the construction phase, involving three contracts; the site work, statue fabrication, and stonework that included the mural wall. My role as the PM included all three contracts. The construction team handled the day to day efforts on the site work, while the contracting officer made me their representative (COR) on the contracts for the statues and the stonework. As COR, I was responsible for overseeing the work being completed and validating the progress payments to the suppliers.

The work on the memorial was happening in three different locations: the statues in Tallix, New York; the stonework in Cold Spring, Minnesota; and the memorial on the Mall in Washington, DC. It involves some of the most renowned architects, engineers, craftsmen, and high-ranking government officials. This included presidential appointees and veterans of all branches of our military service. The most important to me was my father, who served in the Navy during WWII and was called back during the Korean War.

Traveling to Cold Spring, Minnesota, and to Tallix, New York, were some of the most challenging parts of the program. Traveling to Cold Spring, led to changes in my environment, sleep schedule, water quality, eating of fast food, and other seizure stressors. Having a coworker with me, decreased my worry about having a seizure because they did the driving, and there was someone who could fill in for me at a meeting if necessary. Traveling alone increased my stress level, resulting in partial seizures. On one trip to Cold Spring, I had several partial seizures and came very close to having a full complex seizure, as indicated by the impairment of my speech. Overall, the responsibility associated with managing the contracts was not nearly as stressful as

71

the travel. Another stressor was the fear of being pulled off the project if upper management found out about my epilepsy.

My concerns about having a seizure enabled me to be more effective in working with various people. Often you hear about how people get nervous when they talk to someone in upper management. For me, this seemed easy compared to having a seizure. My rate of speech was excellent for doing presentations. This was becoming a skill set, and it was very beneficial in the next phase of the memorial. It would not be until after the presidential dedication that the most stressful phase of work would begin.

The schedules on all three contracts were met and the memorial was dedicated on July 27, 1995, forty-three years after the Korean War cease fire was declared. It was amazing to be amongst the crowds of veterans and their families and being on the memorial grounds a few hours before the dedication. President Bill Clinton and South Korean President Kim Young Sam did the dedication. I was interviewed a couple of times by a South Korean television agency, to explain the layout and features of the memorial.

KWVM Problems

The next phase of work started six months after the dedication with a phone call from Mark, a project manager with the National Park Service (NPS). It was January 1996, and he expressed concerns about several significant problems at the memorial. The next phase of work had begun. It would continue for four and a half years and involve the highest levels of management, the press, multiple engineering and construction teams, and Congressmen.

The phone call was about forty large linden trees and the piping associated with the return system at the reflecting pool. The trees surrounding the pool were dead, and the return piping on the pool was severed in several locations. People were slipping on some of the polished stone. Visitors were getting hurt because they could not see at night, stepping off the edge of the walkway, and falling into the pool. They stayed dry because the pool could not hold water, but in some cases the incidents required medical assistance.

Later that month, the issues at the memorial made the front page of the *Washington Post* and almost every other newspaper in the country. There was much criticism about the quality of the work and the Army Corps of Engineers. The next year involved investigating and analyzing the design and construction issues and reviewing liability. From this, came a determination that the responsibility in developing the redesign of any upgrades and repairs was on the engineers of the Baltimore District, and the arborist and staff of the NPS. My level of responsibility went above and beyond anything I ever imagined.

Multiple Roles

Initially, upper management took control and developed a quick fix, and all seemed well. It wasn't long before it became known that the techniques being applied did not work. Soon after, the chief of engineering called me into his office for a special meeting, on a Friday afternoon. He had met with his counterparts in the district earlier in the day and wanted to tell me what they had decided. My role was to be the project manager and the design team leader for correcting the deficiencies at the memorial. The project was now a top priority to the district commander who wanted the memorial to last a hundred years. He assured me that his design team was immediately accessible and to inform him of any schedule issues.

The most difficult part was not knowing what the corrective action would entail. My imagination took control allowing the fear of the unknown to run rampant in my mind. The following Sunday afternoon, I had a minor panic attack. A half-hour later came the aura that continued to intensify. I was in my backyard and knew it was impossible to get back to the house before the seizure wiped out my cognitive abilities. There was a tree nearby allowing me to sit in the shade. I recall sitting down and having no recollection of what happened next. When my cognitive abilities started to return, I found myself still sitting and confused about what was around me. It would take several more minutes before I was able to recognize the yard and the house. The speech center of my brain was affected, and there were no words available to shout out for help. As my brain settled and reset, some of my speech returned, and the sense of touch and ability to move my arms and legs was restored. My head ached as I walked back to the house. What happened was kept a secret from home and work. Two more seizures of such intensity occurred over the next ten days, leaving the sides of my mouth and tongue sore from my chewing on them.

The following week, a meeting was arranged with the director of the National Park Service (NPS), a senior executive (SES) position of the equivalent of a general in the army. He reiterated the importance of the Memorial and directed his staff to provide the support needed to assure the memorial would be repaired to honor those who served in the war. The arborist with the NPS had studied from the text of the original designer, rejected his redesign, and was given the responsibility for developing a system to assure the new trees would survive. Tracy was a pipefitter with the NPS and was told to work with me on the piping issues. Mark, their PM, was to assure the new lighting system was sufficient and easy to maintain.

Tracy took me to every memorial in Washington, DC, that had a water system or fountain to see if there was a design that could be applied to KWVM. None of the other memorials had the same type of reflecting pool, so we had to develop a new concept that not only provided the required water flow but would last a long time and be easy to maintain. After many hours we were back at the memorial. I was reviewing the notes taken while at several of the other memorials visited that day, while Tracy reiterated his concerns about the original KWVM design. While listening, I drew five circles on the back of my notebook. One was large with four separates but equally spaced circles inside. The large circle represented a manhole, and the four small circles represented openings that drop baskets would fit inside to collect the debris and leaves that fell into the pool. Tracy liked the idea because the manholes were to be installed outside the memorial for ease of accesses and would not require day to day maintenance. Now what was needed was a design that would make construction feasible.

After presenting the concept to the engineering design team they determined the number of manholes required and the size of the piping necessary to make it work. Tracy went back to his office and had a model of the filter built to demonstrate at a meeting with the upper management to obtain their approval to proceed. Unlike the original design that required constant maintenance, the new design would require service only once a month, or worse case, once a week depending on the season. During such maintenance, the memorial would remain open and operational for the visitors.

The presentation of the drainage system was scheduled with the upper management of the NPS. It was during this meeting that Tracy and many other people learned firsthand about my seizures. Some sketches of the new drainage system had been developed, and a model of a collection basket had been made. I was excited and nervous—excited for the concept was relatively simple and nervous for this was a national monument.

We were half-way through the presentation when the aura started. The wave of nausea intensified rapidly, and I could feel and hear my heart racing. My peripheral vision was gone. The seizure had started and was rapidly intensifying. Panic set-in and overwhelmed me with fear. Fear fed by the knowledge of losing my job and the seizure gripping the fear center of my brain. It was an absence seizure that lasted for over a minute. Everyone thought my pounding on the table was out of frustration when a couple of them started talking during the presentation.

It's amazing how the brain works. I knew what was happening with the seizure and wanted to fight it. It inhibited my ability to recall what needed to be said, as the access to the words in my brain was cut-off. Not having my peripheral vision kept me from seeing of how people were responding. Most were just watching me, thinking I was so angry that putting words together was difficult. They were right in many ways, but it was not due to anger. The words started to return but it was impossible to recall the names of anything. Trying to fully describe the items was impossible let alone talking in a complete sentence. To help, Tracy spoke up and gave the name of the object and finished the sentences for me. This went on for another ten to fifteen minutes, at which point my speech recovered to where a sentence could be completed, but I was talking considerably slower. Fortunately, the upper management was impressed with the fix we presented, and the concept was approved. It took very close teamwork to express what was presented during this meeting. Tracy didn't realize his role in assisting me until much later.

After the meeting, he came over and asked me what had happened. He was concerned and wanted to know if there was something he should do. I explained my epilepsy and that everything would be okay. He said he wished he'd known about it prior to seeing me have a seizure, for it scared him and he wasn't sure if he should have called 911. I was glad he had not because the outcome would have been much different for me if he had. As we continued to work together through the construction of the memorial, he shared with me about a family member who was dealing with an anxiety disorder. There were a lot of similarities between this person and me.

In the meantime, a revised lighting scheme was proposed by a gentleman who had close relations with a Vietnam War veteran. The veteran was troubled by what he had read about the Korean War Veterans Memorial and wanted to propose a new lighting system. The two of us worked closely together to develop a system that would light the statues and provide enough

74

architecturally pleasing lighting along the walkways. Once completed, people could safely visit the memorial at nighttime.

As the design was completed for the renovations, the cost could be calculated, and the finances approved by Congress. Once construction was underway my role was both interesting and stressful, as I had to wear a suit for a meeting with high-level officials or congressional staff, then going to the memorial and wearing a hard hat to inspect the piping and lighting systems being installed.

To bring reality back into my busy life, I received a call from my brother. Our father had been diagnosed with stomach cancer and was not expected to live more than six months. It seemed everything came to a standstill, and the memorial was no longer my top priority. Nearly every weekend, I drove a six-hour trip from Maryland to North Carolina, where my parents lived. According to my diagnosis, I was to die long before my parents. Now I would watch my father die. I fought for control of my emotions, especially as I got in my car to drive home. This raised my stress level even higher, caused changes in my environment, and added to sleep deprivation, leading to more seizures.

Fortunately, during his last few weeks, the two of us talked about life. I learned more of his service in the Navy and what he was now dealing with, physically and emotionally, as his body deteriorated. He reached a stage where walking was very difficult yet told me he still had strength in his arms to hug me. His death came much sooner than expected—six weeks after his diagnosis. Just before his passing, the family was talking about his funeral service and having a flag presented for his military service. I called an associate, who obtained a flag in Washington, DC, and had it presented at the site of the future WWII Memorial and the Korean War Veterans Memorial on the Mall. They sent it overnight mail, and it arrived the day before Dad died. He was bedridden and had no strength to move or talk. When we presented the flag, I leaned over him in his bed and gave him a hug. He struggled to get one arm over me and whispered "Thank you" in my ear as tears streamed down his face.

Dad's death took me away from the office for nearly two weeks, and the reconstruction was moving rapidly. With 70 percent of the reconstruction of the reflecting pool complete, the lighting system went from fabrication to installation. Now I had to be in the field a couple times a week to oversee the progress of the lighting system. Soon after, the construction inspector on the reflecting pool was assigned to an overseas program and I was asked to take on his responsibilities. This would require being in the field several days a week for fourteen to eighteen hours a day.

I tried to decline the offer because of my seizures but could not share the fact that I was living with them. Furthermore, I was best qualified based on my knowledge of the memorial redesign and the lighting systems. To make matters worse, I lived north of Baltimore and would have to drive through two rush hours. Outside of my seizures, there was no reason for me not take on the responsibility and, because of not being able to disclose this, management assigned the role to me.

The work required being on site at 6:00 AM., when the construction started, and to be ahead of the snarling traffic conditions typical of the DC area. The lighting system was installed during the day and checked at nighttime. Being the May–June time frame, it did not get dark enough until 9:00 PM to 9:30 PM for testing and adjusting. It was interesting working on the lighting system and being at the Memorial late into the evening. There were still busloads of people visiting from around the world. They were on different time schedules than we were in Washington, DC.

The date for completion had been published, and we were behind schedule for the weather was not cooperating. The lighting system for the statues was nearing completion and everyone was impressed. Originally only the faces on the statues were lit, now the entire front of was illuminated. An unexpected feature was how the reflection of a statue only appeared in the mural wall after walking several yards past it. A little boy stopped as he came past the first statue and told his parents, "I'm afraid of the ghosts."

The Project from Hell

Between family responsibilities and work, my sleep was reduced to only a few hours' a night. The stress was exacerbated by all the places I had to be, and the high level of attention needed for the memorial. At lunchtime, I would separate myself from the rest of the construction teams and try to think about something else for a moment. This helped me reduce my stress level and decrease some of the feelings of anxiety. When this happened, it was not unusual for me to feel an aura coming, impacting my ability to speak for a few minutes or hours. Finding the appropriate words associated with work took longer on many afternoons. Picturing the object being addressed would happen in my mind but the name for it could not be found. No one ever mentioned my inability to remember the names of tools or materials, maybe Tracy told them about my epilepsy. With time this became the norm and pointing to objects worked well, however writing my daily report took more time and often caused much frustration and anxiety as I searched for the words.[*]

A good rapport was developed with the NPS staff, and everyone seemed focused on getting the memorial reopened on time—everyone, but Mother Nature and the rain. Even so, the contractor's staff, NPS personnel and the NAB team worked hard to make it happen. There were no longer any disputes, only problem solving. My days were long; the paperwork and reports were completed during the weekends. The testing of the systems began as we were nearing completion.

I brought Steven, my youngest son, with me one evening, and he was proud to be included. Just like his brother several years earlier, he got to wear a hardhat while at the site. My sister-in-law helped by driving, decreasing my concern about transportation, especially as it got late at night. It is one thing to fall asleep while driving; my biggest concern was how fatigue was becoming a norm for me, and a major seizure trigger.

---

[*] Access to the internet has made this much easier to cope with.

Over the next six weeks, the work around the reflecting pool was completed, and the memorial reopened on time. The lighting in the statuary was complete, and the work on the mural wall lighting had just started.

Two months later the lighting system was completed and the work at the memorial complete. A coworker was with me that day and provided transportation in a government vehicle. On the way home, he watched me pound on the dashboard and cry. He never understood this was my way of releasing the anger associated with my fear of seizures. When arriving home, I was scared to relax, because releasing tension was a trigger to an intense seizure, however, it still came a few days later.

Ten years later, the owner of the lighting company talked with me about his experience working on the memorial. He asked if I remembered what I said that motivated him to complete the work and make sure it was his absolute best. I thought about all the different things that we could have talked about and was totally confounded by what the right answer might be. He went on to explain the time when we had taken a break from work and were sitting against the backside of the mural wall. He said, "You looked totally exhausted. We had been quiet for a while and trying to cool off in the hot weather when you looked right at me and said, 'This has been the project from hell.'" He thought the hell was all the work, schedules, and bad publicity. My response was to explain that those were the problems; the hell was living with my seizures.

He went quiet for a moment then went on to say he was motivated by my dedication to the project, even though it was so hard on me. If I was this dedicated to the veterans and the people who visited the memorial, he could not let them down either. Although he was aware of my father dying a few months earlier, he was not aware that my twenty-year contract with God had reached the end. This was a very difficult time exacerbated by my two young boys—five and seven years old—whom I dearly love. I thought that a seizure would come and kill me soon.

A few weeks after the memorial was reopened and the lighting completed, Mark, my POC with the NPS, sent an email with an article from the *Washington Post* attached. The *Washington Post* had been very critical of what happened with the memorial and the time it took to get it repaired. This article was different, it focused on the two memorials to visit at nighttime. The memorials referenced and reviewed were the Lincoln and the Korean War Veterans Memorials.

Loss of Friends and Coworkers

Within a few months of the completion of the renovations to the memorial, three of the key people who worked with me had died. The first was Ron, who was responsible for the construction contract negotiations and contract documentation. This takes a lot of effort few people are aware of. Ron had been treated for melanoma for several years and missed one of his checkups. When he saw the doctor again, the melanoma was found in his scalp and had spread into his brain and body. He said it was stage four and died a few months later.

The second was Mark, the project manager with the National Park Service. He was diagnosed with a rare liver condition that developed just weeks before the memorial was reopened. He was able to come down to the memorial and see the completed systems with everything fully operational. He died a few weeks later. He was known for his kindness and work to make the Mall a beautiful place to visit. Many of the flower beds along Independence Avenue are of his design.

The third was Christine, my supervisor and mentor. We had worked together for several years, and she provided the guidance and experience for me to move into a management position. She died of a relapse of breast cancer. Revisiting the memorial was now very difficult for me. The motivation to do so did not return until walking past it during the Epilepsy Foundation Walk on the Mall in 2009.

Other Projects and Stress

~~My stress level decreased significantly when~~ Once the KWVM was completed my stress levels lowered significantly, and my seizure activity decreased ~~immensely~~ dramatically. Later it was learned that with each seizure a little more damage was done to my brain. My ability to regain control came when the work stress decreased significantly.

Then came the terrorist attacks on the World Trade Center and the Pentagon, and security was being upgraded at all the army posts throughout the world. I was assigned to be the project manager on upgrading the security at the army posts in several states. Most of the contracts involved lighting, security booths, and pop-up barriers that could stop an automobile instantly. Complexity of the programs increased because there were no barrier systems available to apply to large volumes of fast-moving vehicles. Being the first agency to develop and test such systems brought on the stress, especially since I knew that innocent people could be killed by these developments.

The pop-up barriers consisted of large steel wedges that would suddenly come out of the ground, creating a steel wall. Videos of the testing of the barriers showed trucks hitting the barriers at 45 mph and being stopped immediately. The cab where the driver sits was crushed by the materials in the storage area. Passengers in cars would be severely injured or killed. At this time, there were no alternative barrier systems certified for use.

After award of the contracts, new safety measures were issued requiring signals and delays to the activation of the barriers. None of these had ever been constructed, and our contracts became the test ground for all the posts within the US. As the first gates were completed, with the safety features included, it was discovered that some of the safety features created a significant issue too.

Then there was equipment failure, resulting in the barriers deploying at the wrong time and a few automobiles were damaged. Fortunately, no one was seriously injured, for the vehicles were not travelling very fast. I was receiving calls from several facilities reporting deficiencies in the equipment. As the issues were forwarded to upper management, no direction was being provided on what should be done. Knowing what could happen to innocent people unless the failures were addressed caused my stress level to increase significantly.

Another important project assigned to me was the amputee recovery center at Walter Reed Army Medical Center (WRAMC). Military action was underway in Iraq and Afghanistan, and the number of wounded soldiers coming to WRAMC had drastically increased. The amputee recovery facility was needed in a hurry. A cohort was assigned as the project manager, and I became the design manager. The importance of, and motivation in supporting the troops helped in the design being completed in half the time usually required. The construction cost proposals came in above the funds available, and then WRAMC was to be closed in the next Base Realignment and Closure program. Due to the need and importance of the project, Congress quickly approved construction of a temporary facility.

The amputee recovery facility purpose was to enable the wounded to be fitted for and learn to use their prosthetic arms or legs. To meet the tight schedule and limited funding, a new solicitation package was required, and the package advertised for construction. The work associated with this helped me cope with the stress of dealing with the barrier system contract by keeping me very busy with meeting the needs of our nation's soldiers.

It was amazing to see the wounded soldiers at WRAMC and their ability to recover. Races were held for those with prosthetic legs, and several participants were missing both legs. It was tough to see a soldier meeting with his wife and holding his baby child, with both his legs missing. Those being outfitted with a prosthetic were suffering from multiple wounds to other parts of their bodies. The staff was devoted to these soldiers and the wounded motivated one another to live.

My stress level continued to remain high, however, my tolerance for stress was declining rapidly. Over the next few months, the stress associated with the projects became magnified many times over by the fear of having a seizure, typical of people living with epilepsy. My neurologist had no other medications available for treatment and seizures were occurring several times per week. The epilepsy center at Johns Hopkins Hospital had been recommended and my treatment focused on determining if brain surgery (lobectomy) was my best option.

A week before surgery came a change in command at the district, and I was directed to write a letter addressing the issues with the barrier systems for the new commanding officer to sign. The letter stated the facts as he requested guidance from his protégé at the district responsible for coordinating the program. The barrier work was cancelled soon after, and the contract work stopped. I was not present when the letter was sent and when direction was received to cancel the contracts. The contract for the construction of the Amputee Rehabilitation Center was awarded, while I was at Johns Hopkins Hospital recovering from a lobectomy.

Section 5
Intractable Seizures and Surgery

There is nothing else I can do. You need to go to Johns Hopkins

When my seizures continued to break through the protection of the medications several times a week my neurologist told me, "There is nothing else I can do for you, Jon. You need to go to Johns Hopkins [hospital]." Having been on nine different medications and combinations thereof since being treated at Hopkins fourteen years earlier, he told me surgery may be the most viable treatment. He then gave me the contact information of the epilepsy center. My internal medicine doctor provided the referral needed for the insurance and arranged for me to have an MRI to present to the neurologist during my first visit at Johns Hopkins. Looking at the MRI while waiting for the appointment had intrigued me because there were so many images of various sections of my brain; they had to indicate something.

Initial Review

When Dr. Krauss walked into the exam room, he recognized me right away. However, it took me several minutes before my brain recalled who he was. He had worked with the intern who provided care for me fourteen years earlier. The last time I'd been at Hopkins, my elevated stress levels were driven by the caring of a newborn child and potential job loss. This time the levels were much higher because of the intensity of the seizures I was having, memory loss, and a growing fear of isolation.

Within moments of looking at the MRI, Dr. Krauss recognized the seizure trigger points in my brain. These were the lesions on my left hippocampus, which is part of the limbic system located inside the temporal lobe. After showing me the MRI, we reviewed the options available for treatment. These types of lesions or scars were typical trigger points for people who suffered from high fevers that caused seizures. The options were to continue to try to find a combination of medications that may be affective for a limited time, or surgery. Dr. Krauss did not think medication would be effective based on the number of years it had been applied and how the seizures had become nonresponsive to it. Although he did not say it, I knew that surgery was the best option and asked for more details.

Lobectomy

Based on the types of seizures, and the lesions identified, a lobectomy (removal of a section of the brain) seemed to be the best form of treatment. The unanswered questions were "Did the MRI show all the locations of the cause of the seizures?" and "What would happen to my ability to function when the surgery was over?" Dr. Krauss proceeded to describe the tests that would be required to verify the trigger point to the seizures and validating that surgery was the best treatment.

In some ways, this brought a feeling of relief by knowing about the lesions but was also frightening because of the unknowns of brain surgery. Would I be able to learn and recall information? Would it really stop my seizures? Dr. Krauss explained that there was a 60 percent probability that surgery would stop the seizures. However, the numbers presented did not to take into consideration the level of education and responsibilities of the person having surgery. If I decided to have the surgery, I would be the first of my education and work experience, as an engineer, to have this form of treatment performed at John Hopkins Hospital.

Brain surgery is not to be taken lightly or to be compared to other types of surgery. The brain is the control center of the entire body, and whatever happens to it may affect the personality of the individual. Although it may appear that brain surgery has corrected the problem, the person's personality could change. I cognizant of how treatment affected one's personality through the side effects of some ASDs that resulted in losing control of my anger. Unlike an ASD where my personality could return by not taking it anymore, the effects of surgery would be permanent, or so I thought. Fortunately, there was a series of test that would help in determining the outcome.

Long Term Memory Loss

Dr. Krauss then asked a series of questions that seemed relatively easy. The first was "Who was the previous president of the United States?" I said, "Carter." It should have been Clinton. George Bush was the current president, but I could not recall the name of Vice President Cheney. I was nervous and afraid of the outcome, and it aggravated the problems with my memory recall. This confirmed that more of my brain was damaged since my previous treatment at Johns Hopkins. While learning about the option of brain surgery, I thought about *The Silver Skates*—the Mary Mapes Dodge story with the father having reversible brain damage. Maybe having brain surgery would improve my memory.

Pretest

At that time, there were four major steps to determine the extent of the surgery and the impact it may have. The first was a more detailed MRI of my brain. An MRI of the brain required the whole body to go into a narrow tube headfirst. I found this easier to handle by keeping my eyes shut and remaining calm; I even fell asleep once. The second was a PET scan, which is like an MRI with color that provides more information on the activity of the brain. Then a WADA test was performed to determine which side of the brain was most dominant in my daily functions. The hardest and most intense was a week of monitoring with a continuous EEG and visuals held at the hospital. The choice of proceeding with surgery depended on the outcome of the test and my willingness to proceed. Overall, it would be a lesson in humility as I became more dependent on others, followed with despair and hopelessness.

Dr. Krauss then discussed what was expected of the surgery and some of the side effects. Often patients lost 10 percent of their vision in the eye opposite the surgery. He explained how the nerves in the eyes cross over as they travel to the optical lobe in the back of the brain; therefore, the nerve attached to my right eye goes back through the left side of the brain where the surgery would take place. The area affected was at the top of the eye, and he joked about my days of dove hunting and professional baseball were over. He also explained how the world would become a brighter place, emphasizing the need to wear sunglasses when outside.

My recovery from the surgery would take six weeks for the bone and skin to heal. Up to two years of medical treatment would be required prior to considering changes in my medication. In addition, it would take a considerable amount of time before I was allowed to drive. The amount of time for recovery would influence my ability to function, and work was in question for at least a few weeks to a month or more. Being a project manager and working with people from various backgrounds and positions, made me wonder if I would be able to comprehend all the facets of multiple projects and provide direction to the staff after the surgery.

Making the decision on having the surgery took only a few minutes because my life was now inundated with seizures. The possibility of losing my job was becoming more realistic because of some memory loss and fear. Nearly having had a major car accident with both my children in the vehicle awoke me to the reality of my condition. I had to consider the effect my situation was having on my loved ones and friends. Seizures now dominated my life, and my losing control was leading to isolation and severe depression. Suicidal thoughts were coming more regularly and lasting longer. I was not thinking about killing myself—I just could not find a reason to keep living.*

Journaling

Dr. Krauss recommended that I keep a journal of my seizures. This helped me realize they were occurring two to three times per week. Most were the absence-type where consciousness is lost for several minutes and needing sleep to fully recover. Every day there were several auras that often lasted for only a few seconds. I used the Navy term *pinging* when having one of these. I based it on having a submarine test their sonar near my boat, because it was loud and rattled the hull. Although it lasted for only a moment, it got your attention. I used this term with my work cohorts so the word "seizure" would not be overheard by other people in the work area.

My memory was not the same and I often forgot the names of many of my coworkers—people I saw and talked to daily for years. Finally, after mentioning the seizures and memory issue to a close friend, he responded, "This explains why you have that flat look in your face several times a day." He went on to explain how my normal expression disappeared and became flat, while looking straight ahead for a moment. The seizures were occurring more often than I was aware of. Panic attacks were becoming more frequent and finding basic words more difficult. For instance, when my wife asked me where the children were, I hesitated because I could not find the word *bed*. Eventually, I could say, "Asleep."

While struggling to determine if surgery was the correct treatment, I had a dream. In the dream, I was asked, "Are you willing to help other people?" I was nervous and scared and

---

* This is known as having suicidal ideations, a condition where suicide is being considered, but nothing is planned to carry it out.

thought that there was no way for me to help anyone because of my seizures. My response was, "I can help thirty people." The voice responded with, "You can help 330,000." I immediately woke up and wondered, *with my seizures, how will I ever help so many people?* From that moment on I was determined to have the surgery. The answer to my question wouldn't come until three years later.

A Week-Long EEG

February came, and it was the time for the week-long seizure monitoring at the hospital. My wife went with me to the hospital and we checked in on a Tuesday morning. And after going through all the administrative paperwork, we were escorted to a room on the seventh floor. As we stepped off the elevator, I looked down the hallway and saw the main monitoring station at the entrance. My room was on the right side just past the monitoring station. I paused at the entrance to the monitoring room and looked around what was to be my home for the next seven days. There was a camera system in the ceiling, a bed, a chair, and a bundle of wires at one end of the room. Off to one side was a small bathroom with a toilet, sink, and shower. There was a clock above the TV, I noted it was 11:30 AM.

Another wing of the hospital could be seen from the window and on top of that building was a helicopter landing pad for emergency patients. We did not see or hear from anybody at the monitoring station, and Becky left at 12:30 PM to take care of our boys. Soon after she left, a helicopter landed, and they brought someone in. A strong feeling of anxious came over me triggered by the thought of being locked away and left by myself. It continued to increase and then the aura started, overwhelming my emotions and my heart raced. I was sitting in a recliner and remembered to be sure my legs were straight in front of me. The clock was out in front of me; it was exactly 1:00 PM. Seconds later I was out of it. The seizure progressed for the next twenty minutes, which I based upon when my vision returned and saw that it was 1:20 PM. I was confused as I tried to surmise where I was. Within ten minutes, my ability to comprehend where I was returned; I was at a hospital but could not recall the name of it. It would take a few hours before I could remember the name of the hospital and the reason for my being in the room. I do not know if my speech was impeded for no one had come to orient me.

At 3:30 P.M., a neurologist I'd never met before came to talk to me about my recent history of seizures. He asked, "When was the last time you had a seizure?" I told him, "At one o'clock today." He was shocked, "Why didn't you hit the call button or let someone know?"

My response was, "Because no one told me about it, and with my seizure I may not have been able to remember to do so." He was very frustrated and heard him say "I can't believe we missed a seizure!" several times. He immediately had a technician come in and attach the electrodes to my head; forty electrodes this time, nearly twice as many as in previous EEG test. I was wired to the wall now with a twenty-foot tether and for the next five days, could not leave the room. Any privacy was gone, due to the constant surveillance and EEG monitoring. Whenever I felt a seizure come, there was a button for me to push to inform the staff. A nurse or technician would race to the room and make sure I did not hurt myself or require emergency support if my breathing or heart stopped.

The environment and my situation led me to feel severely depressed. For the next week, I was literally wired to the wall and monitored night and day with a series of cameras and microphones to record my seizures. There was some privacy in the bathroom, but bathing was limited by the wiring on my head. Having several button-down shirts allowed for a change clothes.

In some ways it was comforting to know the medical staff was there in case something did go wrong. My medication was reduced, and we waited for seizures to come. At least three significant seizures would need to occur to enable a determination of where the seizures were starting and how they spread through my brain. Not every seizure would be detected because the skull protects the brain and creates interference that inhibits measuring any minor spikes in the brain's electrical waves. Two more auras occurred later that afternoon but did not register on the monitor.

The next day was Wednesday, and I had two seizures and a panic attack. When feeling an aura was coming, I immediately pressed the notification button so somebody would come and witness what was happening. Several times there was the aura with no detection in the system. That evening, a complex partial seizure occurred, and consciousness was lost. A staff member rushed into the room and watched me.

On Thursday, at one thirty in the morning, the intensity of an aura suddenly awakened me. Remembering there was a microphone in the room I said, "I'm having a seizure." I lost consciousness prior to finding the notification button. The next morning my mouth was extremely sore. My tongue and side of my mouth were injured from chewing that occurred during the seizure. A nurse noticed through the monitor that I was awake and came into the room to ask me how I was feeling. After telling her about my current condition I asked about the seizure that occurred early in the morning. She had not been on staff at the time and went back and checked the monitoring system. When she returned, she told me that I had a very intense seizure during the night. They were able to videotape it through the infrared camera and had the data of the EEG. The seizures were getting more intense as the medication level in my body decreased with time.

Now I noticed that there was little difference between an aura and a panic attack. With both, there was an increased heart rate and anxiety peaks, and both affected my speech. The auras started in my stomach with a wave of nausea, and the panic attacks started with a sudden high level of anxiety. The remaining question had to do with the relationship between the two. Both were affected by the part of my brain where the lesions were. It seemed the panic attacks were a type of seizure too.

That afternoon, the staff asked if I wanted to be part of a study that involved a mental evaluation and test of people with epilepsy. This consisted of an IQ evaluation, memory recall, reading, and math skills. The test was not required, and there would be no charge. The purpose was to develop an understanding of how people with epilepsy adjusted and functioned. They told me I would be the first engineer to ever consider having a surgical treatment for seizures at Johns Hopkins. I volunteered, and it was important because it established a baseline to see what the impact the surgery would have on my cognitive abilities. It was more effective than I thought as the outcome of the surgery was not what was expected, and a record of my mental abilities was now available for comparison.

At 1:00 A.M. on Friday, I had a seizure that left me confused and with a headache. Later, when I woke up at 6:30 A.M., I was disoriented, and a nurse came to help me figure out where I was and what was happening. Just before dinner that evening, I was talking to a friend on the phone and was getting stressed about some issues on one of my projects. I felt the aura come and told him I had to hang up and would call him back. He asked if a nurse had come into the room, and I calmly said, "No, I am about to have a seizure." My last memory was of hitting the notification button before slipping away into the darkness. The ictal stage lasted nearly ten minutes, there was a nurse in my room watching me and talking to me. I could not answer immediately, but my ability to speak returned thirty minutes later. It took over an hour for me to recall the name of the hospital and another three hours to remember to return the phone call. My associate was very concerned because he had not heard from me and was about to call the hospital. I told him it took this long for my memory to reset and remember what to do. He was relieved to know the seizure occurred in a very safe place.

Becky visited me on a regular basis, and my youngest son, Steven, came once. It was difficult for the boys who, in their early teens, were struggling with their father being in the hospital and considering brain surgery. My oldest, Wes, was totally against it and feared I would never be the same or would die. Epilepsy and surgery can be traumatic for the person diagnosed with epilepsy and have equal or even more effect on the family members. Wes had to take on the responsibility of the caregiver as he witnessed me have many seizures starting at a very young age. He did not want to come to the hospital and have a memory of his father being "wired" to the wall.

Saturday was the toughest day for me. I had been isolated for nearly five days and had four seizures over the past twenty-four hours. I battled with depression as the reality of my seizures was becoming known. A friend came to see me that afternoon and was shocked by what he saw. From his perspective, he saw a close friend who loves to be outside, now tied in a room with a series of wires attached to his head. He stayed for a little while and suddenly mentioned that he had to leave. He could not take what he was seeing.

That night, I attempted to watch a movie about the death of Christ. The movie was gruesome, and I did not make it to the end. The anxiety set in, the room seemed to get even smaller, and there was total darkness, except for what could be seen on the TV. An aura started. As the nausea intensified, the TV screen got smaller and smaller and seemed to drift away.

I have no idea how long the seizure lasted but it left a lasting impression. As I regained consciousness, I started to cry uncontrollably. I was beaten and lost hope. This was my fourteenth seizure in just over five days—the fifth significant seizure to be fully recorded.

The Dream

I had not hit the call button this time because my memory was badly impacted. Even so, someone had to come to help me. He was about my height, and unlike other staffers, wore plain clothes and had a large wooden cross hanging from his neck. He approached me cautiously and then came closer. I wrapped my arms around his waist and rested my head against his stomach. I cried hard. I was totally overwhelmed. He said nothing and held me. Seeing the cross, the peace in his face, and his willingness to hold me brought hope back into my life. When I stopped crying and let go of him, he looked directly into my eyes and said, "It's OK. It is part of His plan." I knew then to have total faith in God, and having surgery was only a part of my journey in life. Although I met many of the staff, I never saw this person or anyone else dressed in his manner again. In fact, he was the only person who ever came in and held me.[*]

The following morning, on Sunday, the neurological medical team came and told me it was time to go home, one day early. They had witnessed enough of my seizures to be able to make a recommendation on the treatment. My medication was increased to the normal level, and driving restrictions were imposed for several months. A technician came in and removed the wires from my head. I was elated as I now had the freedom to move beyond the walls. I needed a long shower, to get the adhesive from the wiring off my head. It felt terrific to be clean and able to walk out the door. The ride home was exciting as I could see everything around me. Our golden retriever, Copper, frantically wagged his tail and met me as I walked in the door. My boys ran over, and we hugged each other dearly. The testing provided a whole new appreciation of everything around me.

The WADA Test

A few days later, we met with the Dr. Krauss and learned that the EEG confirmed the location of the source of the seizures. The next test would determine the impact of having a section of my brain removed on my personality.[†] A WADA test, named after the doctor who created it, was used to determine which side of the brain is the dominant side and controls language and memory. To make this determination, each half of the brain is separately anesthetized, and the person is asked a series of questions.

The engineer in me was fascinated in the application of the test and wondered how they would be able to apply the anesthesia to one side of the brain at a time. The video screen the anesthesiologist used to install the shunt was right beside me. Although my leg had been anesthetized locally, it was amazing to watch the shunt going through me yet feel nothing, for there are no nerves on the inside of our bodies that would sense this.

Once the end of the shunt was near one side of my brain, they moved me to another part of the room where a team of doctors and specialists were waiting. The anesthesiologist injected a medication into the shunt and one side of my brain went to sleep. The technician from the

---

[*] Studies have found that such spiritual connections often happen to people with temporal lobe seizures.
[†] Improvements in MRI imagery and neuropsychology testing have since replaced the standard use of the WADA test.

neuropsychology section asked a series of questions that seemed easy to answer, yet what I heard myself saying sounded like my mouth was broken. The words barely made sense even to me. After four basic questions and identifying some objects, I was moved back to the video monitor for the shunt to be relocated. It was pulled back several inches then fed through a different artery to the other side of my brain.

Once again, the same procedure was performed. Apparently, I was able to speak clearly and more precisely, but have no memory of what happened. Within a few minutes, the anesthesia wore off, and my mental abilities returned. The neurologist and the technician started to walk away when I asked, "When will the test begin?" They looked at me and laughed because the test had already been completed. From the moment the left side of my brain was asleep, there was another part of my brain in control which I could not relate to. This side performed well as my speech was uninhibited and answered appropriately—the problem was that I had no short- or long-term memory of what happened.

The rest of the procedure was simple; it involved removing the shunt and securing area of my leg where it was inserted. No movement was allowed for nearly an hour to allow the blood to clot where the artery had been cut.

While travelling home, a flood of thoughts overwhelmed me. I was intrigued by the techniques that were applied for the test and the number of people required for the procedure. The equipment and the skills of the people involved were beyond what I ever thought possible. I was also scared of the outcome and the recommendations the neurologist would provide. I wondered, *if they took out my left hippocampus, would the person I know be gone?* Some of the answers would come the following week through my appointment with Dr. Krauss.

Dr. Krauss was excited to see me at the appointment because of the results of the test. He explained the results with word memory, math, and reasoning when the left side of my brain was anaesthetized. When the right side was anaesthetized, my ability to do math was affected as I mixed the sequence of the numbers. I could not find the words for a *protractor* or a *peacock*, and my speech was slurred. To have a section of my left hippocampus removed made sense, and my response was immediate, "please schedule the surgery."

Self-Treatment

The surgery was scheduled for May 15. At work, I talked to my supervisor, who was aware of my seizures and some of the problems I was having, especially with transportation and having difficult days performing many of my tasks.

Remembering my assignments had become more difficult. When the topic changed in our discussion, I struggled to understand what was being discussed, if I was able to at all. Controlling my seizures required a drastic increase in the AED dosage, leaving me worried about the damage it was doing to my liver and kidneys. It also changed my personality because the old Jon, who rarely got angry, would verbally explode over seemingly insignificant things.

All I needed was to be able to survive for the next five weeks until the day the surgery was scheduled. Surgery was now my only option for treatment. Would I be in the sixty-percentile and my seizures stopped or in the forty-percentile requiring medication to maintain control? My hopes for control and my future were placed completely on the surgery and in prayer.

The Amputee(s)

Five days before surgery, I had a meeting at work with Rick about the contract award of the Amputee Rehabilitation Center at WRAMC. Rick worked in the construction division and struggled with cancer in his leg for many years. His leg was now three times the size of his other leg. Like my situation, there seemed to be only one answer: surgery.

He was sitting in his cubicle, staring at his leg and struggling with his emotions. He felt broken. He didn't even recognize me standing in his doorway, so I asked him what was happening. He continued to stare at his leg and fought back tears as he explained having to have his leg amputated. My response was "That's easy. I'm having a section of my brain removed on Monday." His head jerked up as he quickly looked at me with an expression of disbelief. That's when he learned about my having brain surgery to get control of my seizures. We stared at each other in silence for a minute and then both began to laugh.

The longer we laughed, the harder we laughed. Neither of us had laughed that hard in years. We laughed till we cried. We laughed at ourselves and our situations. Each of us had felt sorry for ourselves and now discovered someone who had it just as rough. He was smiling as he got out of his chair and walked over to shake my hand. As he approached me, we did not merely put out our hands; we embraced each other. We laughed once more and wished each other the best with what our futures held. Upon returning to my office, I realized we never addressed the questions on the project that needed to be answered, in fact they weren't important to either of us anymore.

Family Support

Over the weekend, my wife and I tried to celebrate our twenty-fourth wedding anniversary. It was hard because surgery was scheduled for Monday morning. On Sunday afternoon, the pastor of my church came to pray with me and to learn more about what was to happen the following day. I had no idea if I would be the same person as before or if a part of me would die. Yet I had faith that everything would work out. Prayer was a powerful tool that got me through the situation.

I wrote a letter to my sons in my notebook for them to find if anything went wrong. I wrote this:

> There will be anger and frustration in life, but do not let these become
> you. Use them as guides and never give up hope. You are gifted and can
> do whatever you like with your life. Stay focused and use life challenges
> as a guide to build a good and strong character. Never let disappointment
> get you down for long.
> Love Dad

Chapter 9

Surgery

As long as I have an ounce of hope, I can get through this

It was the Sunday night before surgery, and the hospital was very quiet, especially in the neurology test center where an MRI was to be performed to establish the mapping points for the surgeon to follow. Tags were placed on my head that were to remain until after surgery. Once more, my body went into the isolated narrow tube of the MRI. The tags were to help the surgeons follow the map the MRI created of my brain.

The morning of surgery was relatively simple at the hospital. No breakfast, and report to the patient check in center. An escort would be provided from there to take us to the surgery center. This seemed odd in some ways. The previous visits were for test and consultation. Now it was for the surgery that would hopefully stop my seizures. There were no more decisions to be made and there were no other options if I wanted to continue to live a full life.

The most difficult part was saying goodbye to Wes and Steve that morning. They were on their way to school and knew what was going to happen to me. None of us knew fully what to expect and they were very afraid of what was about to happen to their father.

The surgery was delayed by four hours due to another emergency procedure the surgeon was performing. Late in the morning, I was taken to a room to change my clothes into surgical attire. Another pastor of my church came to see me in the pre-surgery prep room, and my wife was able to follow her in. She prayed with me. I struggled with my emotions as I said goodbye to Becky and taken into the preparation room.

In the preparation room, the anesthesiologist talked about the process of applying the anesthesia and had me sign some documentation. My fear of losing *me* had not abated. We had no idea who I would become after surgery. Having a section of my brain removed could impact my abilities to remember and recall anything, or it could change my personality altogether. Would my soul still be with me as I was transformed? As the anesthesiologist put a mask on my face and started to give me a general anesthesia, I followed his instructions and started to count backward from one hundred. I made it to ninety-eight. This was all I remembered for the next twenty-four hours, even though the doctors talked with me later that evening to check my cognitive abilities and responses and my wife and sister-in-law both chatted with me before going home.

Surgery

The surgery started with cutting the hair off along the tract where the incision would be made. The pattern was like a question mark starting in front of the bottom of my left ear, going toward the back, then following the cowlick, and stopping in the front at the edge of the hairline. The skin was then pulled down, exposing the skull. A saw was used to cut out a rectangular section, approximately one-and-a-half inches high and three inches long. It was placed in a special formula to protect the bone from the air and kept it alive. This exposed over half of the left temporal lobe. Over a third of the forward section of the lobe was removed, creating access close to the center of the brain and exposing part of the limbic system. The lower section of the hippocampus, the center of the seizures, was exposed.

He removed what could be seen and then followed it up into the brain, removing most of it, and leaving a burrowed hole where the hippocampus had extended toward the top of the brain. The void created was filled with a fluid, and the section of my skull that had been removed was set back in place. Two nails were driven through the back of my head to keep the section of bone from slipping into the void where part of my brain which was removed used to be. Four circular plates with five tabs projecting outward were set over the corners and screws were run through the tabs and into the skull to keep the bone in place.*

The biopsy revealed that the hippocampus had hardened and was minimally to non-functional. The hardening was the outcome of many seizures and, in engineering terms, welded the neurons together. Imagine a bundle of wires with damaged insulation that causes an electrical short, generating enough heat to melt them together.

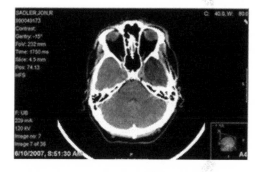

Post-surgery

On Tuesday, the day after surgery, I was monitored in a low-level Intensive Care Unit (ICU). There was an object attached to my face. That object was part of a respirator and it was so uncomfortable, I pulled it off. Then some lady who was near me said something and put it back on. I had no idea she was a nurse who specialized in the ICU and for me to comprehend what the breathing mask was for was impossible because I could not remember what she said. She must have been getting frustrated with me, for soon after she returned to the monitoring station, I'd take the mask off again. This process happened time and time again.

Later they told me about an MRI that was done soon after surgery to make sure there was no internal bleeding. There was none; however, an air bubble was discovered. The mask was

---

A bundle of nerves associated with touch on the left side of the face had been severed. They grew-back together over the next several months but not exactly as they should. Being touched on that side of the chin is felt at the top of the head.

being used to give me oxygen to make the air bubble go away. It was a lesson on what is meant by the term "bubblehead."

Later that afternoon, I was moved to a regular room for a couple of days of monitoring and recovery. The recovery team told me to push a button along the inside the bed if the pain from my surgery became too unbearable. There was another button I could push to call a nurse. Yet due to my surgery, I did not have the ability to remember such directions. A few hours later, the pain was starting to become uncomfortable, and I could not remember to push the button or how to call the nurse. The pain was not from the work on the brain; it was from the area of the skull and skin that had been cut opened. With no short-term memory it was impossible for me to recall what to do when the pain became intolerable.

Before lunch several neurologists came to check on me. They asked me the same basic questions.

"What is your name?"

"How old are you?"

"What day of the week is this?"

"What is your wife's name?"

"Where are you now?"

"What is the name of the hospital?"

Fortunately, I could recall my name, and especially Becky's name. It would take another day for me to remember the day of the week and that the facility was a hospital, but I still could not remember the name of it. They would tell me, "This is Johns Hopkins Hospital." The question was repeated a few minutes later and I still could not remember "Johns Hopkins." Eventually I learned to recall part of the name by associating it with my own—Jon and Johns. It would take several more weeks to recall the whole name. The neurologist who worked with me in my week of EEG monitoring came several times and seemed disappointed.

Impact to the Senses

My first meal after surgery was a lunch that consisted of a salad and hamburger. It had been over forty hours since the last time I'd eaten and my stomach was empty, however my interest in any food was minimal. The hospital staff thought it essential and wanted me to eat. As I bit into the hamburger it brought about a very strong taste of salt and I remember wondering why a nutritionist would give me such salty food. As it turns out, my sense of taste was temporarily impacted by the surgery and swelling of my brain; salt was the only flavor that registered in my mind and was therefore intensified a hundred times over. The salad seemed buried in salt too. In my frustration, I threw part of it off the tray. I would have tossed it farther but could not remembered how to throw. Dinner was lasagna that felt like it burned my mouth and throat. It was not from the heat; it was how my brain registered the taste. Assembling the words necessary to convey the situation was impossible, and Becky and the nurse were very concerned about my reaction.

Cognitive Testing

After the third or fourth time of requesting assistance with the pain, my inability to remember how to apply directions given to me became a concern to everyone. The psychology department was called to perform a test of my cognitive skills and memory. The test was relatively simple and consisted of pictures of items someone of my background should easily identify. The ones I could not answer were pictures of a protractor, a compass, and a trellis—essentially anything associated with engineering. I recognized them; but could not find the name of the objects, indicating significant memory issues. When it came to names, I did well with family members; however, I could not remember the name of my neurologist or surgeon or even the hospital. I felt dumb, and the pain in my head was now intense. The technician could not allow me any pain medication until the test was complete, because it could affect my memory and cognitive skills.

The technician told Becky about my need for extensive therapy that would start in a couple of weeks. I disagreed but ```1 could not find the words to express myself. It seemed as if they were in my memory somewhere, however the access was cut off. The nurse came in and once more explained to me how to apply my own pain medication. For the next twelve hours, the nurses provided the pain medication. After that, Tylenol was given at mealtime and worked well. That afternoon, my sister-in-law brought me a chocolate milkshake, and it tasted great. Later that evening, I asked the staff for ice cream. They gave me both vanilla and chocolate, and they tasted wonderful too.

Applying Math

Dr. Krauss came to see me later in the afternoon. After asking me how I was feeling, he asked, "What's one hundred minus seven?" I could not comprehend what he meant by one hundred or seven, let alone minus. After a few minutes, the number ninety-five popped into my mind. I was unsure what the answer was; however, ninety-five seemed to register with the question being asked, so I said, "Ninety-five." Suddenly, this felt incorrect and said, "No, that's not right." Another minute went by, and the number ninety-three came to mind. I said, "It is ninety-three." The doctor then asked, "What is ninety-three minus seven?" Again, the numbers made no sense, then suddenly the eighty-eight came and I said "Eighty-eight." There was a sensation that eighty-eight wasn't correct, and said, "No, that's not right." The number eighty-six suddenly appeared and seemed correct, even though the immediate thought was, *what is eighty-six?* I said, "Eighty-six." The doctor said, "What is eighty-six minus seven?" My mind comprehending the magnitude of seven and could recall all the numbers starting with eight, from eighty to eighty-nine. Taking seven away from eighty-six was less than eighty, but what was the number before eighty? After what seemed forever, the seventies came, and I answered, "Seventy-nine." The doctor then said, "Minus seven." My brain was stressed, and I was getting tired, but the number seventy-two came quickly, and I answered. "Minus seven," and the sequence of numbers that came before the seventies required a short period of time to recall. Then the number sixty-five came, and I said, "Sixty-five". Immediately I heard, "Minus seven."

The number sixty was not enough, and suddenly the number fifty-eight registered, and "Fifty-eight" given as the answer. "Minus seven." I immediately said, "Fifty-one." "Minus seven." By this time, my head severely ached, and my body was exhausted. After answering with "Forty-four," the doctor said it was time to take a break. Both of us felt a sense of relief as the numbers were restored in an active part of my memory, and I fell to sleep.

Recovery

Late that evening, the surgeon came into my room and removed the catheter. He then told me to slowly sit up and helped me get out of bed. My balance seemed off and I feared falling while standing beside the bed. We talked about tit for a few minutes, then he said, "Let's go for a walk." I had some difficulty getting started, and he held my arm. It was exciting to be able to move. We slowly did a lap around the nurse's station when Becky came, saw me walking, and smiled. She was pleased to see me out of bed and walking. I was excited too and asked the doctor if she could do a lap with me. He was pleased about my motivation and had Becky stand close to me as we started down the hall. It felt good to move even though my head still hurt considerably.

The next day started with a team of doctors coming into my room and doing another examination. Once again, I could not provide any names of the doctors or of the hospital. Later, the surgeon came and asked me what his name was. I could not tell him, so he took his glasses off and asked me to identify the parts. Instead of saying *bridge*, I said *nosepiece*. I could not come up with the name for the hinges or frame. The lenses I identified as glass. He was using the parts of the glasses as a way for me to remember his name, Lens. The process he introduced me to would not take hold until several weeks later.

I was kept an extra day due to concerns with some of my blood test. This was associated with not eating for several days, and not the outcome of the surgery. My eating improved as my sense of taste came back. My ability to taste had mostly recovered along with the memory of what good food really tasted like, and I now rated the hospital food as edible. I was looking forward to being discharged and disappointed in having to stay another day. How I missed my family.

Thursday came, along with going home. My headaches were now tolerable, and I could smile again and couldn't wait to see Wes and Steve. Before leaving, a manager on the hospital nutrition staff came to get my opinion about their service. I wanted to talk about how my surgery impacted my sense of taste. The old Jon wanted to put everything into a brief synopsis of each meal, the quality of the food, and when it was delivered. I struggled for a while, trying to put the first sentence together. The idea was there; but the words to express it were not. After realizing the words to express the details would not come together, I looked at the technician and said, "It sucks."

She was so surprised by my response being so blunt she did not know how to respond. She eventually apologized and asked me to share some of the details. Becky then explained my surgery and my difficulty in putting sentences together.

A few hours later, I was discharged from the hospital. Surgery brought a whole new perspective of the buildings and people we passed on the way home, even the colors in the sky. It was like seeing it all for the first time and being appreciative of the ability to do so. I was excited to know my older sister, Susan, who lived in North Carolina, was waiting for me at home. She would be shocked when we saw each other.

After walking into the house and being greeted by Copper, the golden retriever who seemed very pleased to see me, Susan gave me a hug asked how I was doing. It took less than a minute to tell her everything that happened over the past few days. We were both shocked by my incredibly fast rate of speech and the amount of information I shared in such a short moment. She stood staring at me, and her mouth fell open as she had difficulty registering what was said to her. I was shocked too, because it was in complete sentences at a rate of speech twenty times faster than ever before. The words came to me without any thought. Everything made sense if you could conceive what was said at such a rapid pace. Imagine taking a recording and speeding the playback way up, like what you hear at the end of an advertisement on the radio where they speed up what they have to say to be within the time allotted. That was how I was speaking. I have only a brief memory of what was said.

The boys returned from school and I was beaming with joy. I recognized everything about them, knew their names and could remember what occurred with them prior to surgery. They were so happy their father was home. Their dad had returned both physically and mentally.

Chapter 10
Recovery (2006–2009)

Though my body appears whole, the operation and control center of my brain is damaged. It can only be fixed by the demand to rewire . . . work with me

To explain the outcome of the surgery to my friends, I had them imagine a library consisting of hundreds of floors with staircases and hallways that provide access to thousands of files at each level. Looking up from the first floor, there could be seen the various walkways at the entry to each level with ladders extending from one floor to the next. Each floor has rows of files lining the walls of corridors that extend deep into each level.

The surgery in my brain left many ladders torn from the wall, damaged file cases and torn files laying everywhere. As you look further, you see more levels of damaged ladders, some impossible to climb. Others will take a lot of effort and time to scale. Most of the files still exist, only there is no longer any access to get to them. It seems difficult, if not impossible, to get to the appropriate levels to store or retrieve information.

A week after surgery, I could read a sentence; however, the words made no sense. I could not remember anyone's name outside of close friends and family. Five days after surgery, Susan was reading the comics in front of me, and the Word Scramble problems could be seen upside down on the back of the paper. When she was done reading the comics, she asked me how I was doing. In response, I answered all four of the word scramble problems. She was shocked again, for this was my first time looking at a word scramble.

The left side of my head still hurt, and for some reason it was difficult to straighten my right leg, like the muscles were torn, typical of having a grand mal seizure. It made me wonder if a seizure occurred during the surgery, when my body was restricted from moving and would have resulted in torn muscles. My memory was a mess. And during the second week, I could only recall the names of two of the twelve people working in my office. The others would take over five weeks to return.

I found Sudoku in the newspaper after the third week and doing the puzzles seemed a good idea to try. The first level issued on Monday took a couple of hours to complete. On Tuesday, the next level was issued. This would take several attempts and many corrections. I gave up on Wednesday through Friday for they were too difficult. Pushing myself for hours made my head hurt, but I refused to quit. It would be several months before I could do the highest level, and I felt even better after learning that this was difficult for most people. Exercising my brain was like doing a heavy physical workout, it hurt. Within a few hours, I was exhausted. Sleeping ten to twelve hours a day and taking naps was typical through the first month.

During the fourth week, a friend from church had me go with him as his job required travelling around the county. The people he introduced me to intrigued me as most wanted to hear my story. Often the words necessary to complete a sentence took time. Other times the words came out of my mouth very quickly, and everyone struggled to remember what was being said.

Word Recall

Within a few weeks from surgery, school had ended for the year and we went to the beach for a week. It felt great to walk on the beach, even though activities were limited, such as no swimming or sailing. I started to regain weight as my sense of taste and appetite improved. My taste had changed, the many vegetables and other foods that I disdained prior to surgery now tasted good. My head no longer hurt, and my attraction to Becky started to recover.

Prior to surgery, I was predominantly right-handed. After returning from the beach my interest in fly fishing returned. Without thinking about it, I picked up my fly rod with my left hand and started doing a practice cast. It took some time before realizing I was using my *left* arm and reaching my target with little effort. I did equally as well when casting with my right hand. Curious as to what was happening, I ran into the house, picked up a pen with my left hand, and started writing. It was amazing how little concentration was required and how natural it seemed. The only difference between using either hand was how tired my left became after a short period of time.

Brain Exercise

Things were going slowly with the memory recall part of the recovery. Naps were still required after doing something that made my brain have to work, like reading. With my engineering I attempt to understand what was happening and, fed by a strong faith, refused to give up. There had to be a means to access my memory.

Just prior to surgery, I learned to play "Amazing Grace," on the piano. Now, as a challenge to myself, it was time to memorize the words, written by John Newton in the 1800s. The words brought a spiritual meaning to me in many ways, just not through the same type of life events as Newton experienced. It would take nearly a month of repetitive writing, reading, and singing to remember the first stanza:

> Amazing Grace how sweet the sound
> That saved a wretch like me
> I once was lost, and now am found
> Was blind, but now I see

The words most difficult to remember were the descriptive ones and the nouns. I had no difficulty remembering the title "Amazing Grace" or the tune to the music. It was the words *sound, wretch, lost,* and *found* that I had difficulty with.

As I worked to memorize the words, others came back to my memory. It was like building a new ladder to get to the appropriate floor of the library in my brain. Building the ladder took time and a determination to do so. The effort included sorting through the damaged files and opening the ones that were still whole. New paths would develop to access the information. This required a lot of effort, and the paths seemed to close off when tired. The more tired my brain became (even now), the more difficult it was to recall the words. Tiredness and sleep improved with time. The neurologists said recovery would take up to two years. For me it would take closer to ten.

Fear Impulses

Rediscovering how my brain worked, helped with understanding the panic attacks that overwhelmed me when venturing outside the house. Flashbacks of being in the hospital or immobilized in an MRI unit were common. The fear of not being able to breathe came daily because my nose became stuffed from hay fever. As simple as it may seem, I could not remember to breathe through my mouth. Everything was amplifying one of the fear centers (amygdala) of my brain that may have been exposed or even removed with the surgery. I would taste foods when not eating, smell things that were not near me, and feel like there was a hole in the back of my sinuses. The side of my head began to feel strange. I would later learn these were simple seizures that affected my senses. *

Nerve Reconstruction

There was a bundle of nerves that was affected by the surgery where the scalp and skull were cut open. As my head healed, the nerves began to come together, and the sense of touch was returning to an area around the left side of my mouth and chin. However, they were not reconnecting in the right order. Touching my chin or flossing my front teeth brought a tingling feeling along the upper left side of my head.

Pushing myself harder lead to discovering ways to get my memory back. Although my body was not tired from the brain exercises, my brain was. The auras came back, and the fear of having a full seizure brought my heart rate up. The aura often ceased when stopping what I was doing and walking away from where I'd been. The setback was that I was having more auras after surgery than before. The benefit was that I was not losing consciousness. My brain was healing.

One evening, a neighbor asked me about how my recovery was going. We started to talk about what had happened with seizures and surgery, and she kept wanting to know more and asked detailed questions. An aura started that raised my anxiety level, and my heart raced. I told her we had to change the subject because of my not feeling well. She started to ask me what was happening, and I walked away to change the environment and not have to recall what I'd been through. I was conscious the whole time, and within a few minutes, the aura stopped. It still left me with a sense of fear.†

---

* Simple Focal Seizure that effects a part of the brain and the senses
† An indicator of post-traumatic stress disorder (PTSD).

Loneliness

I needed someone to talk to about what was happening—someone who could relate to what I'd been through and what was happening now. Telling my family about the auras would make the surgery seem like a failure, and they did not want me to have it done in the first place. There was no one I could talk to who could relate to what epilepsy was like, (Mark had been taken off medication and had not had a seizure in years). Walking with Copper to the woods nearby gave me a place to hide and cry aloud. My prayers focused on my needing understanding on what was supposed to be done with all this. The darkest time of my life was thought to have occurred prior to surgery, and now it was getting even darker. There had to be a meaning and a purpose to my experience.

I learned more about this through memorizing the second stanza to "Amazing Grace." It did not take quite as long as the first—only about two weeks to memorize. The words in this stanza applied more to the current situation. I was buried in the fear of the outcome of the seizures and surgery, when all that was needed was to believe, and the fears would be relieved.

'Twas Grace that caused my heart to fear
And Grace my fears relieved
How precious did that Grace appear
The hour I first believed

It was difficult to sing the first and second stanzas together. It seemed it would take three to four attempts to sing through both without missing a word or hitting a dead end in my brain. The phrase *dead end* seemed to make sense, because my memory would go down the old path and come to the end created by the surgery. When this happened, I had no idea how the song would continue, and the resulting frustration magnified the problem.

My regaining control depended upon exposure to the things that were triggering my mind to go into the panic mode. I returned to my workplace at the Corps of Engineers to let people know more about my absence. A partial seizure came while coming up to the secretary in the chief of engineering's office. My aura started, and impacted my ability to speak, the words I wanted to say were gone. She started by saying how nice it was to see me again. I could not respond. She went on to explain how she was the only person in the office at the time, all the managers were in meetings. This was a good thing, for it took a few minutes before the words could be assembled to respond. This was my first complete simple focal seizure after surgery.

I returned home quickly and sat on the couch in disbelief of what happened. In some ways, it was good, for the secretary would let everyone know it may be a while before I'd be able to work at the office. However, I was very discouraged because my case was not in the sixty percentile of the people being cured.

That afternoon, a friend was taking me out to the Scout camp where Steve had been camping for a week. This could not have come at a better time, and it would be good to be with him in a setting away from home. My fears subsided as my mind became busy with something more important, and I was in a safe area with a friend and my son. It was time to work on memorizing the third stanza of "Amazing Grace."

Through many dangers, toils, and snares
I have already come
'Tis Grace that saw me safe thus far
And Grace will see me home

The frustration caused by having more seizures and memory issues no longer dominated my mind as the words in the song came together. The levels of achievement were lowered, for the ability to remember any of the three stanzas was considered a success and made me smile. The frustration I felt when I was not able to recall all three dissipated. When recalling all three together actually happened, it made me smile more and I would cheer quietly. And it seemed like the occasions to smile were happening a lot more often.

Psychological Testing

Through the recommendations provided by the speech therapist soon after my surgery, I returned to Johns Hopkins Hospital Neuropsychology Department for testing. It had been three months since the surgery. The neuropsychologist interviewed me and was impressed with the level recovery and reminded me I had about two years left to fully recover. We all looked forward to seeing the results of the test.

The parts of the test that seemed extremely difficult involved remembering names and identifying objects. I had scored low prior to surgery in the thirty percentile. This time the score was the lowest possible—in the less than one percentile. My verbal memory and retention of what was being told to me had declined. Prior to surgery, I could glance at a code of eight digits, consisting of numbers and letters, and type it into a computer without having to look back again. Now remembering two-digit numbers was difficult, aggravated by my often reversing the numbers. Identifying objects was also difficult. I could not recall the names of any items associated with engineering, such as "compass," "protractor," or "trellis."

The fascinating part was that my ability to problem solve had improved. This was with figural learning, where my cognitive skills of hands-on application had immensely improved. For instance, although I wouldn't always choose the correct answer, I had written out the correct manner to solve it. My ability to solve problems had improved slightly. This was very important in my recovery. My memorization and reading comprehension were poor to begin with, but now those skills were even worse.

The most amazing part of the test results was how my brain was working faster than before surgery. With the damaged section removed, it was able to process information significantly faster. I could even talk faster now. At the end of the test and the interview, it was determined that my own manners of treatment were enabling my brain to heal and have good control over my cognitive abilities. It would just take time, maintaining a positive attitude and creating a demand for my brain to map new ways to find and recall information.

Neuropsychological Performance

Surgery May 2006

	Preoperative February 2006	Postoperative July 2006
General Intelligence (IQ)	87th	88th
Language		
Naming	31st	<1st
Fluency: Initial Letter	10th	9th
Fluency: Category	32nd	9th
Verbal Memory		
Total Learning	16th	5th
Delayed Recall	4th	14th
Recognition	55th	10th
Figural Learning		
Total Learning	62nd	90th
Delayed Recall	82nd	>93rd
Recognition	>16th	>16th
Processing Speed	58th	70th

Interview

A few weeks later, the neuropsychologist contacted me to see if I would be willing to share with the hospital staff the outcome of my surgery and what it was like living with epilepsy. Every week, the staff of the neurological department would have a conference meeting during lunch and would appreciate interviewing and learning more about me. I immediately agreed, even though I was still dealing with agoraphobia. The only way to recover from this fear was through more exposure, and this presented a good opportunity. On the day it took place I arrived at the neuropsychology office to talk to the director. After updating him on my recovery, which were to be used in my introduction, we proceeded down to the conference room. The stage was the lowest point, with the seating rising on a very steep incline. This allowed everyone to easily see the people being interviewed. Another advantage was those on the platform could easily concentrate on one another and the subject matter, because only the first couple of rows of people could be seen unless you looked up by tilting your head back to see above yourself.

The format of the meeting was reviewed as they attached a wireless microphone to my shirt. The assistant chief of the neurological department was to do the interview as the chief was not available. The assistant chief and I were to sit on the side of the first row until introduced. Then we were to walk to the center of the stage, where there were two seats facing each other. All I had to do was pay attention, follow the lead, and answer the questions to the best of my ability. The neuropsychologist was to be informed if I became too nervous, which had happened with speakers who had been patients, and he would not require me to participate.

The hall began to fill up as it got closer to the start time. I recognized the lead neurologist and neurosurgeon who worked on my case and some of the nursing staff. The lighting was dimmed as the session started. The only section with lighting was the stage. Then a picture of my brain, over six foot by six foot, appeared on an overhead screen. I was mesmerized by it as the Chief of Neuropsychology talked of several other items of the week and then proceeded to talk about my case history. We were then introduced and proceeded out to the chairs on the stage.

As the introduction was being made, I became extremely nervous, and my hands started to tremble. Auras came while looking at the picture of my brain. Fortunately, they lasted only ten to thirty seconds, and I never feared they would progress into a full seizure. They made me ask myself, "Do you have the ability to get through the interview without having a seizure." Once seated on the stage, the interviewer demonstrated a manner of kindness and appreciation that helped calm me down. There was nothing for me to defend or explain like often happened when talking about construction projects. They only wanted me to share my experience, and this allowed the amygdala, or fear center in my brain, to calm down. This brought back memories of chairing meetings involving numerous engineering staff, customers, and upper military staff, and the old Jon was back. This newfound confidence enabled me to look up into the audience and find the staff involved in the various stages of my treatment and enjoy talking directly to them. As we ended, I was asked for any recommendations I could give the staff. I replied that it wasn't a good idea to feed someone a hamburger so soon after surgery and be aware of the impact surgery may have on a person's short-term memory.

When the time came to leave the building, I felt much better and believed my recovery was underway. Rewiring the brain takes time. Like learning a line to a song, it requires multiple attempts and repetitions. Although my fears were calmed in front of the group, they quickly returned and seemed magnified as I left the building. It would take several more years of exposure and academic study to regain consistent confidence and become a leader again.

Church Support

The leadership in the Reisterstown United Methodist Church, where I had been a member for several years, assisted in my recovery. I was asked to join one of the pastors in a meeting with several other people. She started the meeting by reading Matthew 17. This was about Jesus being transfigured on the mountain, where two of his disciples are with him. Then they see his face shine like the sun and his clothes became pure white. They hear the voice of God, and Jesus tells them not to be afraid. The reading continues as Jesus comes off the mountain and sees his other disciples with a crowd of people:

> [14] And when they had come to the multitude, a man came to Him, kneeling down to him and saying, [15] "Lord, have mercy on my son, for he is an epileptic[c] and suffers severely; for he often falls into the fire and often into the water. [16] So I brought him to Your disciples, but they could not cure him."

> [17] Then Jesus answered and said, "O faithless and perverse generation, how long shall I be with you? How long shall I bear with you? Bring him here to me." [18] And Jesus rebuked the demon, and it came out of him; and the child was cured from that very hour.

> [19] Then the disciples came to Jesus privately and said, "Why could we not cast it out?"

> [20] So Jesus said to them, "Because of your unbelief; [d] for assuredly, I say to you, if you have faith as a mustard seed, you will say to this mountain, 'Move from here to there,' and it will move; and nothing will be impossible for you. [21] However, this kind does not go out except by prayer and fasting." [e] (New King James Version)

The pastor was using the reading to talk about how we could change if we believed. The moment she finished, she looked at me, and her face started to flush, and her mouth dropped open. She immediately realized the reading included how difficult it was to cure a child with epilepsy and started to apologize to me. The seizures were considered the action of demons until medical technology was developed to the point of understanding the neurological components of the body. She was afraid that I would consider myself possessed by a demon. I assured her that I did not believe this and that everything was fine with what she read. Having never heard this passage before, left me amazed.

The passage intrigued me, and I wanted to do more research. Here was a child with intractable seizures, living in a society that did not understand epilepsy. The only way to explain a seizure was through what was thought about many other medical conditions, that it was an evil spirit possessing a person. "Treatment" in those days, and even now, consisted of rejection and isolation of the person thought necessary to keep other people from contracting seizures too. The boy suffered more from society's view of his condition to the extent he attempted suicide many times by throwing himself into the fire. The actual demonic possession was not in the boy but of the people who feared him, the demon being fear. There are similarities to this story in today's society—the difference being those who follow the medical field understand seizures are not caused by demonic possession. They are due to an injury, structure issue, or chemistry of the brain. The practice of isolation still exists for the same reason as it did in those days, because many people still do not understand epilepsy. In fact, it was troubling for me to learn about church organizations throughout the world and in this country today that still promote seizures and other conditions that effect the brain as demonic possession.

The reading made me start to think about what the boy did when he no longer had seizures. His father witnessed what happened in the child being healed, but did the child still fear having a seizure? Could the child learn and remember new things? Did he use his life as a representation to others that they can keep moving forward too? How would others who witnessed his seizures accept him? The time would come when the answer would be provided to me as events and interactions with other people continued to occur.

I started memorizing the fourth stanza of "Amazing Grace" that included the two most important words in my ability to live with epilepsy, hope and endurance:

> The Lord has promised good to me,
> His word my hope secures;
> His will my shield and portion be
> As long as life endures.

Memorizing the fourth stanza took only a few days. I was smiling more and laughing often after being able to sing all four stanzas. The ability to remember words had come back because of the refusal to give up. The fifth and sixth stanzas came even easier. It was a new beginning.

> Ya' when the heart and flesh shall fail,
> And mortal life shall cease,
> I shall be found beneath the veil,
> In a land of joy and peace.

> When we've been there ten thousand years,
> Bright shining as the sun,
> We've no less days to sings God's praise
> As when we'd first begun.

The church had a men's group and the men prayed, visited, and challenged me. One of the fellows also led the contemporary service and asked me to lead the prayer session at the next service. This was a time when we would have the congregation share their joys and concerns and then pray together. The leader would make a record of what people shared and included them in a prayer. The prayer closed with everyone saying the Lord's Prayer together. I quickly agreed to do this because such exposure was necessary to get over my fears and this was an opportunity to do so with the support of a congregation.

Over the next couple of years, I would do the prayer once per month. It required several hours for me to write something even though it was just a few minutes long. The prayer started with asking the congregation to share their joys and concerns. The biggest challenged came when addressing everyone's joys and concerns as they were presented just before doing the prayer. I tried to jot down the key points, like the name of the person or place that needed to be included. While leading the prayer, my whole body shook with nervousness. Most people in the congregation knew of my surgery, and many would thank me for the example I did not realize I was providing.

The Engineer

With the driving restrictions and recovery expected to take several more weeks, arrangements were made for me to work from home. Trying to do anything on the computer seemed impossible the first few months after surgery, because of not being able to remember how to log in or access the required files and documents. The plan was for me to take four to six weeks off, and during this time my associates called to check on me. The reality of my recovery came as we started to talk about specific projects.

It had been four weeks since surgery when the details of a stressful project were discussed—the Access Control Program with the barrier systems. I could not find the basic names of the equipment we were installing, such as *gate, crash arm,* or *bollard.* I could recall the topic being discussed, but none of the specifics. My head began to ache as the fear of never being able to recover came over me.

Fortunately, the people I was associating with knew about my surgery. The program we were discussing was very stressful, and the person who filled in for me struggled with the documentation of cancelling the projects. Seems this project was jinxed, for within six months he had a grand mal seizure. The cause of the seizure was stress and not taking appropriate care of his physical needs. He had another seizure a few months later and was diagnosed with epilepsy.

When I returned to the office, the plan was to resume my role as a project manager and work on the projects assigned to me before surgery. While reviewing one of the contracts with the Access Control Program, my brain went crazy. A sense of fear caused a panic attack and continuing any work on the program was not healthy. After closing the file and putting it back into the file drawer the aura subsided and went away.

Another difficulty I had was the inability to comprehend the details of the emails I received concerning other projects. Writing responses was difficult and remembering who to call and where to go seemed impossible. After a couple of weeks, I contacted Bruce, a friend who now worked in an upper management position. We had worked together on several projects, and he was someone who could be trusted and made aware of my disabilities prior to surgery. Now I needed guidance on how to inform management about my inability to perform the work I once excelled at. As we discussed some of the projects we both had worked on, he began to realize my ability to recall the details was severely impacted. In order to formally address this, he recommended a letter be provided about what happened with the surgery and my current expectations.

The letter should have taken less than an hour to write and now required nearly a day to assemble and arrange the words to make sense. Even then, the grammar and format were poor, with repetitiveness and incorrect punctuation. A few days later, I presented the letter:

Subject: Jon Sadler's Request and Safety Issues

I have been epileptic for nearly 30 years. The problem was handled well with medication until last year, when I started having more seizures than usual having been through several types of medication. I was able to keep things under control however my medication was so high I started having reactions to the medication.

John's Hopkins recommended surgery. The surgery took place on 15 May 2006. Due to some issues with my memory I was to undergo some additional testing in July. All went well. My medications have been reduced, with further reduction scheduled this fall (with a plan to possibly take me off all medications that I have been on for nearly 30 years).

I continued to have some kind of reaction that was not explained to me until last week. Call me the "Air-Head" for during the surgery a bubble was left in my head.* It caused dizziness after physical activity or being excited.

My preference is to stay away from the PM (project management) effort for a couple of months till my thought processes are tested. As I have explained to others I have had the file cabinets in my head rearranged, including some of the doors locked, walkways damaged and ladders removed. I have found alternate ways to get to the file cabinets and have gotten faster at doing so (the ones with the spider webs don't function due to age not surgery). However, work is going to help fix this and if I can do some writing etc. let me loose. My driving will return in a few weeks; however, it has been over a year since I have driven on any highways and I will need some "training" time before I take off again down I-95.

I have never let epilepsy control my life. I have been physically active and have a family. For work I was the waterfront/utilities specialist for the Navy, budget and cost tracking for a Contractor and you know the story for the Army Corps.

---

* This was an example of my memory issues. The air bubble had to be repeated to me several times after surgery and follow-up doctor appointments.

I've looked for ways to help Hopkins, for the surgery is only 5 years old and I am the first engineer to go through the(ir) process.

Your assistance on this matter is appreciated. If necessary I will take a pay cut or GS level reduction due to the PM issue.

Sincerely,

Jon Sadler

Bruce acted the next day and went to see Jerry, the chief of the contracting division. Jerry had a project that needed special attention, and he did not have the staff to do it. It was perfect in helping me recover my math and organizational skills. It involved evaluating close to four hundred contract modifications. It took me days to organize the documents and weeks to evaluate the numbers. I was transposing numbers and could not remember more than two to three numerals at a time. It would take extra time for me to evaluate the changes. Yet as I worked more and more, my abilities seemed to improve. My review took over three months to perform. My presentation of the materials was clear and concise. Based on the information, the government recovered a large sum of money for overcharges by a contractor. It felt great as my ability to process numbers had returned, and the funds recovered paid for my own salary several times over. The hope that I could be a project manager again returned to me.

Setback

Bruce had another assignment for me involving a presentation to a local chapter of the military engineers. It was a slide presentation with notes to be read on each slide. The session went very well, and I felt great even though a couple of auras occurred just before and during the session. Many of the members wanted to talk after the presentation, but I had difficulty responding because I could not recall the information in my brain. Fortunately, I had to leave early for an appointment with my neurologist at Johns Hopkins.

It turned out my neurologist was not available, and the surgeon filled in. He got excited (and maybe frustrated) when I told him about the auras. He explained how they determined how much of the hippocampus to remove and how he now wished they had taken out a little bit more. The autopsy indicated the section of my brain removed was hardened, indicating severe damage.

An EEG was ordered, and I was to wait in the exam room before heading to the test location. Depending on the outcome, we would talk about having surgery again and other techniques available to remove more of the hippocampus. Inside I felt broken. It seemed impossible for me to go through again what happened the first time. The surgeon said he would walk with me to where the EEG would be performed when they were ready. When he returned, he apologized, for the EEG could not be done for a few more hours and asked me to return to the waiting area.

While in the waiting area I almost broke down in tears as my emotions tried to go rampant. To go through what I had previously experienced, this time on my own, made the thought of going through the pretest and surgery unbearable. I then decided that any more surgery was not worth the risk and pain. Walking back to the receptionist was difficult and scary. They told me the surgeon was available, and to wait by the desk. When he came out, I said, "I cannot go through this again. I'm leaving now." He was disappointed and started to talk about how the EEG would be good for me to pursue. I was torn apart, emotionally. I had given a presentation in the morning, speaking in front of more than fifty people and complimented on my knowledge and abilities. An hour later, I was having to deal with my biggest fear: if surgery was performed again, who would I be when it was over?

The Child with Cerebral Palsy

While waiting for the elevator, there were three people standing near me. We were each told something about our health that seemed to be a major setback. We made eye contact as we waited and said nothing, each engrossed in our own grief. The elevator seemed to take forever to arrive, and when the doors opened, we quickly entered. In the sixty seconds it would take to get to the ground floor, we were all changed by a child suffering from severe cerebral palsy.

She was about twelve years old and in a special wheelchair where she could lay back so her body could straighten. She was completely immobile as her fingers, arms, legs, and head never moved. The only part of her body that could move was her mouth and eyes as she looked at each person individually. When her eyes locked in with each of us, she smiled. When she smiled, her entire face lit up. As she would do this for each of us, we smiled back, and we couldn't help but continue to keep on smiling.

When the elevator arrived at the ground floor, we thanked the girl and her mother for the experience as we walked off. The young lady did the only thing she could—she smiled back. Her mother smiled but could not say anything as she was crying too. She had just witnessed how her quadriplegic daughter helped each of us see our situations in a better way. As the doors closed to take them to their floor, we saw the mother wipe away her tears. The four of us took a moment to reflect and share the effect the young lady had on each of us. Her actions uplifted our spirits so much so that we could now take on the challenges that each of us faced with hope.

First Grand Mal

It had been six months since the surgery, and everything seemed to be getting better. It was exciting to buy a car and be able to drive again. This time I made sure the vehicle had a manual transmission and the emergency brake on the center console in case a seizure came again while driving. With a manual transmission, the car would stall if my foot was not on the gas pedal or if someone pulled hard on the emergency brake. Worst case, they can push hard on the gearshift and knock it out of the drive gear into neutral. It would not be the best thing for the transmission, but who cares when someone's life was at risk.

Soon after getting the car and going on a trip with my family to see my sister Susan in North Carolina, my confidence was shaken. This was the first road trip I was going on since surgery. When we arrived at her home, my nephew was curious about what had been happening to me and wanted to ask about my surgery. As we talked, my anxiety level increased, and I was getting concerned about having a seizure. I tried to change the subject, but he was curious and kept asking questions about the procedure and recovery. He did not realize what was happening and my need to stop thinking about the most traumatic event in my life. I started to have an aura and managed to get it to stop by walking away from him. Late that night, I had a grand mal seizure in my sleep. Becky awoke and shouted for help.

Susan called her friend who was a paramedic and lived a few minutes away. He notified the ambulance team and rushed over to her house. When he arrived, he saw me lying on my side on the floor near the bed and administered oxygen to help me recover. My body was partially blue from the interrupted breathing caused by the seizure. The ambulance team arrived and talked to Wes, who I could see pulling information about my medications from my wallet and talking to a paramedic. Seeing my color return and learning of my seizure history, the paramedics agreed that no further medical assistance was required. I had some level of consciousness the whole time the paramedics were there. My mouth and tongue hurt and there was blood on my pillowcase. As soon as everyone left, I quickly fell back to sleep and slept until the middle of the morning due to exhaustion. Everyone else was up at that point and planning for the day.

There was a change in my recovery this time. Instead of my cognitive abilities needing two to three days to recover, it took only a couple of hours. Recovery of the muscle groups involved still required several days. I was upset at this initially because this was quite a setback. I reminded myself my brain was still healing and recovering from surgery. After breakfast, the boys started to play catch football, so I went outside and joined them. Susan's friend, the paramedic, came by later that morning and was amazed when told I was out hiking with my boys.

Extensive problem-solving, not sleeping eight to ten hours a day, and talking about the trauma of surgery were the healers and the triggers to the seizures. Putting the mind to work required mapping new ways to store and retrieve information. Being motivated through other people was crucial to recovery. I started to cross paths with many who were dealing with epilepsy and other disabilities. Surgery changed my life, just in an unexpected way, and not as I had feared. I could crawl out of my hiding place and be more open about living with epilepsy.

Second Grand Mal Seizure

My sons were still active in scouting, and we discussed going on a trip to the Boy Scouts High Adventure Camp in Philmont, New Mexico. Adult leaders were needed to participate. The trip was not to occur for a couple of years, giving me time to recover from my surgery, coinciding with the two years mentioned by my Johns Hopkins neurologist. It was exciting to be able to go to Philmont again and to sign up to be one of the adults needed to go with the scouts. Within a few months, the trip was moved up a year—less than a year away and just over a year after having surgery.

When a friend from church heard about my endeavors, he invited me to hike to the bottom of the Grand Canyon with himself, his son, and a friend of his son's. It would be an incredible journey requiring five days of backpacking to the bottom of the canyon, over five thousand feet in elevation, to the Colorado River. We would be going in late March—four months before the trip to Philmont. It seemed like a wonderful plan to help me get back in shape and regain confidence in myself.

I almost freaked out when we arrived at the Grand Canyon National Park and could see the size and magnitude of the canyon. Ten to twelve auras an hour occurred as we walked along the ridge. Going down into the canyon meant being isolated, for cell phones lost signal past the first few hundred feet. I was serious considering getting a hotel room to stay in as the others went on the hike. After reviewing my epilepsy with everyone, they assured me they were fine with my going with them. This restored my confidence and the next morning we started the five-day hike in the canyon.

It seemed unbelievable that this was happening. I was able to control the fear of seizures occurring by simply focusing on the magnificence of what I was beholding. Several times an hour, my cohorts heard me say, "This is incredible." After saying it so often they asked me to use some other words like *amazing* or *awesome*. I continued with *incredible*, because I could never imagine that someone in my condition could do something like this, never!

Eventually, we came to a section of the trail where there had been a rockslide and the trail was wiped out. To get through, we had to hang onto a boulder and inch our way around it with a three-hundred-foot drop along the ledge we were on. While coming around, I could feel the weight of my pack pulling me away from the bolder toward the abyss behind me. Fortunately, about the time I was going to slip away, I stepped onto the trail on the other side. My knees were shaking, yet I had no auras. It would have been an incredible trek for anyone, and now I was doing it!

Over the next five days, we saw some of the most beautiful sites in the world and climbed along narrow pathways with no safety rails and drop-offs of several hundred feet. At the bottom of the canyon are beautiful beaches of pure white sand with the roar of the Colorado River echoing off the canyon walls. I got over my fear of heights and stood along a ridge with a three-thousand-foot drop-off to peer down at the river below. During this time, there were no auras or seizures, until returning home, where the change in the environment and elevation triggered some.

I would be vulnerable to having a seizure during the first twenty-four hours of traveling to a new location. Three weeks prior to the Philmont trip, we went to Ocean City. A strong aura awakened me early the next morning. Feeling exhausted I got out of bed and walked around the house we were renting to get a drink of water. I returned to bed and fell right back to sleep. Within an hour, another aura came and awakened me. This one was much more intense. While trying to get out of the bed, I fell and hit my head on the edge of the nightstand. The seizure was intensifying as I lay on the floor unable to move. I could see the side of the bed but could not hear or feel anything.

Becky got up and, seeing me on the floor, called 911. It was early Sunday morning when this happened, and the paramedics and hospital staff assumed the seizure was caused by a reaction to a drug overdose. I could not move or speak while being transported to the hospital. Just as we were turning into the drive to the ER, I could finally tell the paramedic my name. Becky followed in our car and the boys stayed at the beach.

When the doctor heard about my surgery the year before, he ordered a CAT scan. It wasn't until seeing it, that the staff believed everything we said, and that it was not caused by an overdose They could see that the forward third of my left temporal had been removed, and a tunnel existed where my hippocampus was supposed to be. They immediately assessed that the seizure was caused by epilepsy, and that no further observation or testing involving misuse of drugs was necessary.

They then agreed to give me some ice for my eye that was swelling shut from hitting the corner of the night table. A few hours later, I was feeling better and was discharged. As we were getting ready to leave, we asked for a copy of the CAT scan to give to my neurologist.

When we returned home from our vacation, I was prepared to fight with the staff at Philmont about being allowed to participate in the ten-day hike. Their policy was no one could participate if they had a seizure within the last six months. Just before I made the call, Wesley came to me and shared his concern. He had seen me have many seizures. In the last two, he played a major role with getting the appropriate medical assistance needed. He told me how he would not be able to sleep or go too far away from me during the trip for fear of my having a seizure. He saved my life more than once, so I listened to him. He made me aware of the importance of considering how the seizures were affecting my family, not just me. Within a week, the scouts found someone to take my place. Philmont played a significant role in my life through my scouting trip in 1976. Now my seizures kept me from being there with my boys, and I was heartbroken.

Curious as to the extent of my surgery and not having seen any of the scans done at Johns Hopkins, we viewed the CAT scan from the recent ER trip on our computer at home. For the first time, we saw how much of my brain had been removed and were shocked. From a side view, we could see the four circular plates. Each had five tabs with screws going into my skull. In the back of where the skull had been removed were the two nails, about an inch long. The cross-section views showed a cavern where the forward section of the temporal lobe had been removed, providing access to the hippocampus. A path or hole could be seen where the hippocampus used to be.

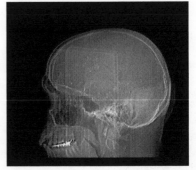

A few years later, we watched the movie *Master and Commander*. There was a scene where a doctor in the early 1800s does brain surgery on a member of the crew. The patient was suffering from a severe concussion and was in a coma. The doctor drilled a hole through his skull to relieve the pressure, then he placed a five-pound gold piece over the opening and nailed it in place. I lamented to my friends that all I got was four quarters, twenty screws, and two nails. Everyone laughed.

One way of coping with my depression while the boys were at Philmont was to build a patio on the back of our house. The energy I had to carry the brick and dig out the area came from the anger and frustration inside of me. I had no problem getting the soil beneath the brick compacted as I pounded the dirt and cried several times during the days I worked on that project. I was angry at God, society, the Boy Scouts, and myself.

Reading Skills Improving

My reading skills were improving, and I discovered there were several books on how people overcame the fear of seizures, along with studies on how the brain works. Jill Bolte Taylor had just published *A Stroke of Insight*. Jill is a neuroscientist who suffered a stroke and had surgery like mine around her left temporal lobe and hippocampus. The first part of the book is about her having a stroke, which has some similarities to a seizure. To help with my recall, I highlighted the parts I found that were most applicable to myself. Over half of the text in the section on recovery was highlighted. Jill did well with everything she planned and worked on. When something changed, she had difficulty remembering and adjusting. The most difficult part was how her brain required eight years of recovery. For me, it would take ten. In fact, recovery continues today as I discover more about myself and my abilities.

The most important part I learned from the book is that recovery will only continue if the brain needs to do so. If there is no desire and need, the brain will not adjust and will acclimate. If there is a demand, the brain will find ways to make it happen. We have over a trillion neurons.

The undamaged will rewire and strive to find new manners of connecting when circumstances require it.

Chapter 11
Overcoming Disabilities

I brought up the coping mechanism to some people lately. Talked about just accepting your issue and moving on, instead of WOE IS ME. I used our morning laugh sessions with Steve. You were the half-wit, I had no leg to stand on, and Steve (lazy eye) stared at, I dun no. But to me it's still a good object lesson of when beaten down, LAUGH. So, if the Right Hemisphere was itching, it was ME, PEG LEG

—A text to me from Rick after one of his group sessions with people dealing with

amputation

The people at the Army Corps of Engineers believed in and were helping me with my recovery. Bruce was excited as he did a review of my recovery and learning about the contractor returning a large sum of money to the government. He had a team working on cleaning up ordnances and an oil spill at a site and needed my help. The site had been used for testing mines (explosives) up through the Vietnam War. It was a large area being prepared for placement of a facility associated with the latest Base Realignment and Closure program. The contract was awarded at $8 million, and the work had just started.

We did not know the amount of the materials involved in the cleanup, and the contract was based on actual cost the contractor experienced while performing the work. As more and more of the area was surveyed and materials uncovered, more men and equipment were required, and the cost increased. The field team called every day to report finding another area with buried waste that required cleanup. Within twelve months, the project grew to over twenty million dollars. I took on the role of project manager and coordinated with the post staff the costs incurred and estimates of the additional work in order to obtain the required funding.

My biggest challenge was reversing the digits in the numbers as I entered them into a computer or wrote them down. For example, $1,250,750 would be clear in my mind yet I would write down $1,520,750. This caused a fair amount of confusion as the totals were never correct. Some figures were left reversed, even after I reviewed the numbers over and over. The best technique for checking the numbers was suggested by my work associate. He was partially dyslexic, and his biggest challenge was arranging words properly in the reports he wrote. To correct this, he read aloud what he was writing. The computer took care of the spelling and punctuation issues.

Initially, I found this very annoying and asked why he had to do it. He explained how reading aloud enabled him to recognize the order of the words being out of place or a word missing in his sentence. I went from being annoyed to becoming motivated, because the reading out loud enabled me to verify the numbers and make the appropriate corrections.

The project was completed within a year. Management then had me move to a section in the construction division responsible for evaluating contract proposals. This would be a major challenge for my brain for the evaluations were on multimillion-dollar projects and were very extensive and detailed. Reports ranged from thirty to a hundred fifty pages. This was where Rick worked. And when he learned I would be working with him, he was relieved. He remembered the day we looked at each other and laughed over our situations and upcoming surgeries.

There was another person nearby who had a wandering eye known as strabismus. Each morning, the three of us would get together and talk about the challenges we faced. Then we would help one another understand ourselves and, most importantly, laugh. The nicknames we had for each other were mostly kept between us.

Chapter 12
Exposure

People with disabilities have the ability to not be disabled

First Counselor

It had been nearly three years since my surgery. To help with my adjustment and recovery, I tried to find a counselor who could understand what I was going through. My first counselor worked in a room where she dimmed the lights and had a background noise that made me uncomfortable. She seemed to be overwhelmed with what was shared and just "oooh'd" and "awed" in her responses. Within twenty minutes, an aura occurred. I thought, *this was worthless* and not helpful at all. It took a couple of years before I found a counselor who helped guide me to reach out to others.

In Front of the Crowd

Wes and Steve were in a competition band at their high school, and I volunteered to be on their pit crew team to build and bring the backdrops on and off the field. The competition involved high school bands consisting of sixty to one hundred students that performed on the football fields at schools from all over the region. Travel could take up to two hours in each direction. The competitions took place on Saturday evenings, and it was not unusual to get home after midnight. I figured it would be good exposure to people and crowds and to be with my boys.

Nearly twenty parents volunteered to be on the pit crew and we usually had approximately five minutes to set up the field displays for the band and three minutes to take them down. The backdrops were twelve-by-eight-foot pictures of the New York skyline. It was fun to unload all the equipment, watch the boys prepare for the competition, and help with getting the equipment on and off the field. Being on the field scared me, especially with such large crowds in the stands. But it was also very helpful as it helped defeat my fear of exposure to people and making new friends.

The second year, the theme was "Fear." There were ten four-by-ten-inch banners with the titles to various types of fear. The type I closely related to was agoraphobia—the fear of everything. The band did very well again and was invited to play in a Disney World parade. My exposure on and off the field reinforced my ability to participate and work with other people. Little did I know at the time the significance of the trip to Disney World. Not only did we get to see the parade, but the parents also got to see the boys play in concerts and enjoy the rides. My ability to travel and participate in the rides provided hope to another family dealing with seizures.

The Young Man with Spina Bifida

One of the members of the band suffered with *spina bifida*, and I was amazed to see how far he had come in his life. My brother, when working on his doctorate in the 1970s, spent time

116

with children suffering from *spina bifida*. During that time, it was unusual for a child to live beyond five-years of age. Through research, they found manners of treating the condition. Now here was a sixteen-year-old, straight A student, who did not let his condition stop him from participating in the band and other school activities. He never thought of himself as disabled.

He played a keyboard, so the pit crew built a platform for him to sit on and play. The band members liked to be around him. And on the days that he got tired of being in his wheelchair, he would sit on the floor in the band room. When he did this, everyone else in the band would sit on the floor too. On the day of graduation, I thanked him for being such an inspiration to me. Seeing his abilities helped me conquer my fears of being in public and inspired me to push beyond my limits to help my brain recover—to demand it to "rewire."

His son was four years old and had intractable seizures.

Sharing Experience

It had been three and a half years since my surgery. My memory was improving, and my confidence was building. There was a gentleman who was doing a survey at the office on people with disabilities who, learning of my having epilepsy, wanted to see me. He had been having seizures most of his life and needed to talk to someone who could relate to what he was living with.[*]

He came into my office, introduced himself, and asked if I had a minute to talk. As he sat down, he told me about learning of my having brain surgery and wanted to share what it had been like for him to live with epilepsy. He had an amazing positive attitude. Like many people dealing with seizures, he never had a driver's license and relied on public transportation. He shared how his attitude changed from feeling guilty and depressed about his dependency on others to feeling fulfilled.

We both had relied on other people for transportation; his assistance came through members of a church he attended. He explained how his dependency for transportation provided an avenue for those people to apply their God-given talents and gifts. This had happened for me many times through the support from my church, and his story helped me realize how a person's dependency was one of God's tools in inspiring others to help. It is amazing how a difficult situation can give a person a new perspective on themselves, especially when the situation makes a person feel hopeless. Having this new perspective made me wonder even more about myself and brought back the question: "What am I in training for?" How was I supposed to work with other people after being humiliated, embarrassed, and fearful of the repercussions caused by a seizure?

The Phone Call

A few months later came a phone call from David in association with a construction project[†]. We were discussing our availability to meet and review the technical requirements of a contract. He told me he was not available the following week because of a family conflict. David was dedicated to his job; however, his priority was to take his son on a Make-A-Wish trip to Disney World. I assured him this would not be a problem and continued to talk about another time which would work for both of us. He then said, "We received a grant from the Make-A-Wish foundation because my child has epilepsy."

Hearing this brought my world to a sudden standstill. Could this be happening? Should I share my own experience or keep quiet? If I share it, will he doubt me and think less of me? For

---

[*] People with brain injury and seizures were not considered as disabled by the Army Corps of Engineers at the time.
[†] Not his real name, for privacy reasons

nearly a minute, there was complete silence as I struggled with myself on what to say, before deciding it was not important for David to know about my condition. Besides, if his child is going on a Make-A-Wish trip, his condition must be severe, and my own experience could not be important.

With the phone being silent for so long, David thought I had hung up or his cell phone cutoff. It was not unusual for him when mentioning epilepsy that people would cut him off by hanging up their phones. He was hopeful it was a phone signal issue and was about to hang up and call me back when I responded, "Your son and I have much in common."

Suddenly, our discussion changed from work to epilepsy. I shared part of my story—of being treated for nearly thirty years with medication and having a lobectomy, affecting the left temporal lobe of my brain. About every five minutes, he interrupted me saying, "But you're a project manager," as he could not believe someone with epilepsy and brain surgery could be in such a position.

It had been less than a year since I had been to Disney World on the band trip with my family. We rode several rollercoasters and seen many shows. It was a wonderful time, everyone in the family got to be a child again, and we got to watch our boys perform on stage and march in the Disney parade. I talked about the excitement of riding the rollercoasters and going to the shows. It had been nearly two hours since we started talking, and sharing experience with a stranger was usually exhausting, but continued because I realized of how my experience could inspire hope in a person.

A few weeks later, we had our meeting, and one of the David's coworkers and a close friend asked if we could talk in private. We went into another room and sat down. The gentleman started by thanking me for being open about my experience with epilepsy and how everyone now had hope that David's son had a future. I fought back tears and had difficulty thanking him for sharing this information. It was overwhelming. This was the explanation to my living longer than the twenty years expected. It was God's way of telling me to reach out with my experience and provide hope to those struggling with the trauma of similar experiences.

Answering the Call

A whole new part of my life was coming together. On the way back from the high school Wes and Steve attended, I stopped by the office of the local Epilepsy Foundation in Towson, Maryland. I had seen the sign many times over the past several years having driven past it on the way to the high school.

There I met Mary Wontrop, the director of the chapter, and expressed my interest in providing support. Within a few weeks, she told me of the HOPE mentoring program which the Epilepsy Foundation had for people who wanted to become mentors[*]. The acronym HOPE stands for "Helping Other People with Epilepsy." Within two months, I received the training and began doing something never thought possible—sharing my story with more and more people.

---

[*] H.O.P.E. is a trademark of UCB, Inc., Atlanta, Georgia, for its epilepsy mentoring program, licensed by the Epilepsy Foundation and its local chapters' use.

This would change over the next few years, from sharing my story to effectively counseling people with seizure disorders.

Applying the Call

During this time, I found a mental health counselor whose practice was very helpful in evaluating my situation and providing motivation and planning for the future. After I shared what was taking place in my life through my work, the church, the epilepsy foundation, and my motivation to recover, he recommended my going to graduate school and changing careers. I didn't think this was possible because of the way my brain functioned with recalling names.

As he learned more about my life, he again and again suggested becoming a counselor. Eventually, he was more specific and suggested my becoming a pastoral counselor—a program offered by Loyola University in Baltimore, Maryland. Learning more about the program, made me more excited and concerned about my brain's ability to absorb the information such a program would entail. The questions that filled me with doubt were "How can a person who can't remember names, get through the studies and the exams associated with courses that are required?" The other question being, "How would I coordinate working full time, attending classes, and completing all the work assignments?" Yet everything seemed to be falling in place for me to do the program.

After visiting the campus and learning more about the program, I submitted my application. The interviews followed and a few weeks later the letter of acceptance was received. With an engineering degree, I did not have any of the requirements completed so there were numerous prerequisites to complete prior to starting the two-year internship and finishing the remaining courses required to graduate. My self-confidence was completely gained from a spiritual calling, because my brain could not conceive of being able to function well enough to complete the twenty-two courses on subjects never studied before. Little did I know that there would be a group of people I was about to meet who would provide the motivation and reinforce the idea that the impossible was possible.

Section 6
Recovery and Graduate School

Chapter 14
Graduate Degree in Pastoral Counseling (2010–2015)

The impossible is possible!

Although Loyola University was founded by a Jesuit priest in 1852, the pastoral counseling program did not focus on Christianity alone. The students, instructors, and professors were of different backgrounds, faiths, and religions, including Catholic, Hindu, Buddhist, Islamic, and various Protestant faiths. Some people were not associated with any religion; yet they had a strong spiritual connection with God. Others were priests, chaplains, or pastors; titles of leadership based on the religion they were associated with. Most of us were on a second or third career and felt a calling through our experiences to provide pastoral care to others.

Unlike other counseling programs, the studies and discussions were expanded to include how God and prayer are important in everyone's life. Appropriate application of a spiritual nature was reviewed throughout all the classes. The counseling internships were associated with various counseling centers, recovery houses, and medical facilities to help us grow and develop into effective counselors.

Most classes started with a classmate talking about an experience or sharing part of a book or poem, that had helped them grow in the understanding how God works through people and is ever present. People with disabilities were given the support they needed in the classes, either by other students or the disability programs provided by the university.

Most of the graduates were working full time and planned to complete the program in three to seven years. The master's degree included studies in humanities, statistics, religion, ethics, and law. In addition, we studied individual, family, and group counseling, social and racial issues, and theories and techniques to apply in various settings. Four of the courses involved an internship in clinical work to develop individual counseling techniques. To work full-time and complete the program was quite a challenge for anyone.

The clinical courses involved working in a counseling facility eight to twenty hours per week, along with additional supervision hours, writing extensive papers, and attending weekly classes. A total of eight hundred hours of clinical work, including 280 hours of one-on-one counseling with clients, was required for graduation. To assure that the interns understood the roles of a counselor, they had to have experience being the client. If interns had not seen a counselor before, they were required to do so for an extensive period to fully comprehend what was taught in the classes. This was the only pre-requisite I'd already completed. My new counselors were the students and staff involved in the program.

Special Assistance

Through the requirements of each course and the people involved came numerous lessons about humility and witnessing survival and perseverance through faith. Several colleagues had experienced traumatic events, and others had disabilities that impaired their learning in a typical class setting. I was humbled, yet witnessed and developed manners on how to ask others for support. In my first semester, I took a course on humanities taught by Professor Frank Richardson. I had told a fellow graduate about my epilepsy and what to do if I had a seizure. She was curious and asked more questions and was fascinated by how I had come in my recovery. She would play a key role in my getting through the program.

Four weeks later, we had our first exam. The format of the exam was relatively simple: fill in the blank at the end of the question. It was frustrating for me that the first letter of the key word to answer a question would come to my mind, but the entire word could not be recalled. When our graded exams were returned, I had less than fifty percent marked on the side, with an F at the top of the front page. My classmate saw this and asked me if I was going to talk to the professor about my disability. I said no because my hopes were gone, and I thought about quitting by the end of the semester. She looked straight at me and said, "After class, you have got to tell the professor about your disability. If you do not, I will." She made sure I did not abscond and when class was over escorted me to the front of the classroom to see the professor. I was about to be taught the greatest lesson on the power of humility.

There were several people in line ahead of me waiting to speak to the professor, and all I wanted to do was leave. However, my classmate wouldn't baulk and talked about the importance of sharing my experience and asking for support. Professor Richardson was a quiet, easygoing person who was vested in getting us through the program. He was an ordained pastor, with a PhD in psychology and many years' experience working with people with disabilities. As I approached him, I felt despondent knowing I would never be able to get better grades with my brain injury. He looked at me and said, "It's good you came to talk to me for I need to know what happened on the exam." I did not know what to say, so my cohort promptly told him that I needed special assistance. Expectedly, the professor's response was "Why?"

Declaring Disability

When I told him about my epilepsy and surgery, he asked, "What is required for you to pass an exam?" I replied, "I need a list of words, and please do not give me the standard *A B C D* form of answering system. Just provide a list of words somewhere on the page, and I will know which is correct. I also need additional time to take an exam. If this can be arranged, it would be very helpful." He got very excited as he explained to me the importance of him needing to know about this sooner. I was surprised because he was not only willing to work with me, but it was also important to him to do so. He went on to explain that the exam we had just taken would not be counted in my final grade. In addition, he told me about the program the university had for students with disabilities and the importance of my talking to the facilitators right away.

On the next exam, there was a list of nine to ten words after each question on everyone's exam paper. It was incredible, for after reading a question, the first letter to the answer came to my mind and I could immediately recognize the correct word, even though several started with the same letter. I needed additional time because to fully comprehend the questions required my reading them several times.

I quickly learned how nervousness caused my brain to shut down before I could comprehend what the question was about or even what the words in the question mean. I could read each word; however, the context of the question would not formulate in my mind. Staying calm was critical. It would take time and practice to learn how to do this and allow my mind to absorb what was happening. I was amazed at my ability to recall the answers and very pleased to earn a low B to high C grade on every exam. Passing the course was now very feasible.

Sometimes the answer would appear in my mind, yet I could not comprehend the importance of it. Prior to the surgery, the answer would come to me, and I could remember it while writing out the sentence or an essay required to express the answer. Now the key words seemed to suddenly appear and then disappear. Often it would never reappear, especially when I got apprehensive or frustrated. This was something that would take time to understand and control, for example, jotting down the key words before writing out the sentence.

Preparing for the tests required many hours of study and discovering techniques to recall names and titles. I had difficulty with such things prior to surgery in 2006, as demonstrated in the testing done during the five-day EEG. At that time, I scored in the 34 percentile, meaning 66 percent of the people in my classification scored higher than me. After surgery, my score went to less than one percent, the lowest rating possible. The harder I tried to remember something, the less I would be able to recall. Frustration would set in, and everything I was reading and working on would go blank (like activating the old path in my mind that was a dead end).

When everyone else finished their exam, the professor would take me to another room, where I would work for another thirty to forty-five minutes. When calm, the words seemed to flash up and sometimes be gone in an instant. With time this would slow down and more than the first letter of the word would appear. Often by writing the letter down and repeating it, the whole word would appear. My level of intelligence was not impaired by the surgery; it was the ability to recall specific words.

The final paper due at the end of the semester had the biggest impact on the overall class grade. The paper was to be based on a personal perspective of our lives and how our experience(s) have impacted our life views. My paper was based on living with epilepsy and discovering how to help others persevere through similar challenges. This is when I learned of the professor's interest in working with people with epilepsy, and especially his willingness to work with me.

He would not share this until the papers were turned in and graded. It was our last class, and he started by sharing more of his background, the experiences he had as a child, and his ministry. His mother had epilepsy, and as a child, he witnessed her have many grand mal seizures. It was during a time when the ignorance of the disorder had led to laws regulating education and marriage for a person with epilepsy in many states. He talked of his mother having a very long seizure while on a road trip. He and his siblings had to make room in the car for her to lie down and recover. While sitting so close to her he found a spiritual connection that helped him survive and thrive in working with other people—first through the church and later as a psychologist. He worked with many people dealing with disabilities throughout his career.

At the end of class, he handed back our papers. I saw the number 498 on the top of the front page, and my mouth fell open in shock. This was out of 500. On the second page was an A and a note about how he related to my experience. He assured me that I could work with the program and wished me the best in my efforts. I was so amazed about the professor's experience and his ability to relate to mine, so much that tears were streaming down my face.

Disability Support

The graduate program for me required learning how to learn. The easy part was working through the Disabilities Office provided by the university. Upon confirmation of my disability through my neurologist, I was able to obtain special services and notifications provided to my professors regarding my disability. Special assistance was received in the form of additional time to take my exams and being allowed to record the classes. This additional time was essential in allowing my brain to search out the answer within my head and was crucial in controlling nervousness. My brain not only had to find and follow the route to the answer but was also required to develop new patterns for the information to be located and transposed for me to write out the answers. Sections of my brain needed to rewire based on the demand to do so.

The accommodations of the Disability Support Office were essential in helping me complete my classes. The grades for the next several courses were based on take-home exams or writing a series of papers. I required many hours to review the answers to be sure the paper related to the specifics of the question(s). The statistics classes required making sure the answers were not transposed. In most cases, the professors were very supportive and worked with me.

There was an excellent writing center that provided support by reviewing and teaching how to write according to the standards required by the counseling program. This was a treasure, for there is quite a difference between how a counselor and an engineer write. The engineer used bullets and preferred going straight to the facts. The counselor needed to express everything in full sentences along with an explanation, with backup documentation appropriately cited. The American Psychological Association (APA) formatting was to be followed. They provided websites that taught how to properly format a document, quote references, and arrange sentences and paragraphs. Writing was frustrating for me because a sentence would come together in my mind, then be lost before I could complete typing it. In some cases, I unknowingly reversed the words. The staff at the writing center assisted with proofreading and providing guidance on documentation and format.

A few of the courses, such as statistics, had open-book take-home exams with no time limit. Everyone thought that my background as an engineer made statistics easy for me. Although statistics has numbers and charts, it is its own language. Furthermore, my mathematical processing ability had been severely jarred through my seizures and surgery. I thought this course would be one of the most difficult for me, so I took it in my third semester of studies to be assured of my ability to complete the program.

In my third year I took a course on Psychoanalysis, where the professor could not see that I had a disability because of my normal appearance and active participation in class discussions.

She couldn't believe I had disability with word recall. However, on the exams, I did well with the multiple choice and poorly on the fill-in-the-blank questions. Going into the final, my grades were not high enough to have the course accredited as completed for the program.

Learning about the diagnosis of anxiety and mood disorders, schizophrenia, and personality disorders was most interesting because they applied at various stages of my life, especially during recovery from a seizure and brain surgery. Some of these symptoms occurred as a side effect of a medication. The reason a person with seizures would not be diagnosed in these categories is the fact that the symptoms are caused by a neurological disorder—epilepsy or induced by medication.

To test the professor's assumption about my not having a mental disability, she made some revisions to the final exam. The exam was primarily fill-in-the-blank-type questions, that consisted of several sentences relating to specific methods and applications of diagnosis. Some of the questions had key words that applied to the answer to other questions. As I was last to finish, the professor and her associate were as curious as myself on the outcome and graded it for me. I missed just one question. This demonstrated my familiarity with the subject matter and validated my disability to express specific names. She then realized how we do not all think alike and that I was not making up my disability. Since the final exam covered the entire course, she gave me an A for the course.

Mental Exhaustion

While going to graduate school I had to continue working full time for the Army Corps of Engineers. There would be those evenings, after a trying day at work or suffering from a lack of sleep, that my memory recall would be affected. There were days when the exhaustion caused my memory to basically shut off and limited my ability to learn or recall a subject matter. When asked a question, I responded with "Sorry, I'm tired and my brain is not here." There were several people in the classes who were dealing with memory issue; however, theirs was caused by being bored or simply not being able to comprehend the material being taught.

This further aggravated the difficulty I had in my taking notes because of not being able to remember what was said long enough to write it down. I could not write as fast as the professor spoke, and my short-term memory would blank out or would mix the words out of order. I would start a sentence then have no memory of the key words or names affiliated with what I was writing about. My best was writing four words in the start of a sentence; there were many uncompleted sentences in my notes. Fortunately, this process was simplified as my poor note-taking skills were assisted by technology.

Electronic Support Systems

Most of the professors had no problem with the class being recorded by a student with the understanding the recordings were solely for the individual and would be deleted upon completion of the course. In most of my classes, this could be done on my cell phone. I would write down a key word and the time of the recording for cross-referencing. It was not unusual for me to spend several hours each week listening to the recordings and completing the notes.

At the end of my second year, Moodle was implemented by the university. Moodle is an online learning management website that enables a student to keep track of their assignments, schedules, and grades. Most importantly, it enabled students to interact with each other electronically and watch recordings of the classes. Applying these tools decreased my concerns and dependency on others and helped overcome memory issues. Recordings allowed me to listen and see more of what was happening during class and, with practice, access my own memory by playing the recordings.

Through practice and demand my abilities improved. After three years, I reached the stage of having a complete set of notes at the end of a class. My brain was working extra hard and was being exercised through replaying the recordings of the classes over and over. This brought me a lot of relief, and hope.

Another very useful tool was the Kindle book. Electronic versions of the textbook were now available with important features that are especially helpful for people with learning disabilities. Taking notes required highlighting the text and labeling the note to save it. I needed to develop a skill to identify what was important and labeling it appropriately. Then Id could access the information through the Kindle program on my computer by going to the notes screen and determining what was most applicable to the class assignment. These notes could be electronically copied and pasted into Word files to assist with my studies and papers.

To help in organizing and writing papers, came the Dragon NaturallySpeaking program. In lieu of typing, a person talks to their computer, and the words appear on the screen. I was no longer dealing with the delay of typing and minimized the loss of my thoughts.

Inspiration

I was still careful about letting people know about my epilepsy for fear of how they would react and associate with me. Then during my fifth semester, a paper was due, and I was exhausted from the late nights of research, writing, and engineering work earlier in the day. My anxiety level was very high, and the person sitting next to me saw my hands shaking slightly. I was having a simple partial seizure and had felt an aura come as a wave of nausea passed through me; however, I did not lose full consciousness. She asked if help was needed, and I responded, "No." A few minutes later, I told her about my epilepsy, and she became quiet. Afterward, she sat far away from me in the remaining classes. She would not respond when I tried to talk to her about a subject matter or simply said, "Hi."

There was another student named Curtis, a pastor who was studying for his pastoral counseling degree, and who had a significant influence on my life. On the opening day of every course, we would take a few minutes to learn about the person next to us and then introduce them to the entire class. Curtis seemed like someone I could trust. As typical when doing such introductions, I shared with him information about my family, work experience, my being in the program, and motivation to become a counselor which included my having epilepsy. Curtis then told me about his background, motivation, and calling to work in the pastoral field with me to share when introducing him. After introducing him to the class, he followed and the first thing he said to everyone was "This is Jon Sadler, and he has epilepsy." I knew he did not intend to deride me since he indicated his fascination of me came through my motivational and spiritual calling.

Regardless of his intentions, however, I felt so ashamed by what he had said that it felt like the only way to look was up. Now everyone in the class knew of my condition and had a reason to be afraid of me, or so I thought. Then I realized that there was no longer anything to hide or fear. Since everyone now knew of my seizure disorder, I no longer needed to worry about how they would respond if they saw me have a seizure. In that moment, I felt taller than I ever had, like the ten-thousand-pound weight of dread I carried all these years was gone. I no longer had to hide my disability.

After class, I felt even more inspired, and now fully understood my calling. Three classmates came to me to ask for help in understanding epilepsy. One had a close friend who was recently diagnosed with epilepsy, and the other two had family members suffering with depression caused by seizures and ASDs. Their love for their family was part of what inspired them to become counselors. I didn't need to say anything as they simply said, "Thank you for sharing your story and never giving up." They wanted permission to share my story with the others to bring them hope through the example I never realized I was setting. After returning to my car and climbing inside I was overwhelmed by what had just happened. It was one of the *ah-ha* moments when all my experience in living with seizures and the doubt and fear of how others would react had deeper meaning. There were more people inspired by my perseverance than those who feared me because of my seizures. I had to wipe away the tears before heading for home.

Curtis provided another insight concerning relationships. He talked of how we each have a path to follow as we journey through life. Our paths cross with other people, sometimes it is just for a moment; other times our paths run parallel as we journey together through a period of life. In long-term relationships, the paths run side by side for much of our lives. On other occasions, we see a person for just a moment. What we do can have a significant influence on their lives and our own. A good example of this was the man who provided me the new license plate in Rhode Island when my license was reinstated. With Curtis, we would journey together for four months as we studied in the same class and would cross each other's path only for a moment after that.

By being honest about my seizure disorder, I enabled others to be comfortable talking about their issues. My classmates taught me more about dealing with anxiety, depression, deafness, abuse, addictions, and stages of spirituality, to name a few. The key components in their lives focused on survival and hope. Everyone was motivated by a calling they received when dealing with something difficult in their lives. Some were living with the challenges themselves, and for the rest, it was being the witness or caregiver to another.

Medical Follow-Up

I kept in touch with Dr. Jason Brandt, the professor of psychiatry and behavioral sciences, director, Division of Medical Psychology and Professor of Neurology at Johns Hopkins University, who was interested in my case and motivated me in my experience in recovery and studies. Most of our communication was through email:

From: Jon Sadler
Sent: Monday, July 23, 2012 4:55 PM
To: Jason Brandt
Subject: Sadler Case

Dr. Brandt,

Thought I should give you an update on how I am proceeding with changing careers. I have completed 9 of 22 classes for my degree in Pastoral Counseling. As you may be aware, the studies involve understanding oneself. Through my volunteer work and studies, I have learned more about the self-generated fear of seizures and the significance of being open and willing. The first few classes required writing papers about having epilepsy from a first-person vantage and the last few from a third person perspective. It has been interesting how the discussions in the classes have brought out quite a few people dealing with epilepsy through relations with family and friends.

Five of the classes have had closed book quizzes; those that are multiple choice I do well with, those that are fill in the blank I do not for my difficulty locating the words (in my head). Fortunately, only a piece of the overall grade is based on the quizzes. So far, the most difficult class was Psychoanalysis which I had this spring, as we studied the DSM-IV-TR. I could relate in a first-person manner to "Anxiety and Mood Disorders," "Schizophrenia," and "Personality Disorders" through my seizures and side effects of medications. The professor was impressed with my ability to provide insight and awareness about making such diagnosis and the importance of verifying the physical condition of the client, medications, etc. (including talking to a neurologist or neuropsychologist). She watched me take quizzes (fill in the blank) and struggle with word recall (I tried several different manners to memorize terms, etc.). I could write a paper indicating a full comprehension of the situation without additional time (OK I was usually last to finish). For the papers, I had access to the manuals/books and knew where to look. The comprehension is there, accessing title through my mental resources was difficult. The last quiz was written in a manner where the wording of the questions related to nearly all the answers (i.e. wording of question 1 had the answers to question 5). I did very well.

My plan is to start clinicals in January 2013 and finish the program in 2015. This will coincide with my retirement as an engineer. Seems the harder I work the better my brain functions.

Hope all is well,

Jon Sadler

He was very helpful in keeping me motivated. The more I studied, the more I could understand what was happening within my own brain. He responded with this:

Dear Jon,

Thank you for taking the time to write and letting me know about your academic progress. It seems that you have a great deal of insight into how your cognitive system works (i.e., metacognition), and your mental strengths and weaknesses. As long as you continue to capitalize on your strengths and minimize your weaknesses, you should do fine!

Keep up the great work!

Best regards,

Jason Brandt, Ph.D., ABPP(CN)
Professor of Psychiatry & Behavioral Sciences
Director, Division of Medical Psychology
Professor of Neurology
The Johns Hopkins University School of Medicine
600 N. Wolfe Street, Meyer 218
Baltimore, MD 21287-7218

Chapter 15
Clinical Work

Challenges in life enable one to grow and take on the future. A sense of joy develops. Joy brings on the ability to grow in dark times. Hope and faith make all things possible

For my clinical requirements, I worked with peopled dealing with drug and alcohol addictions and others with brain injury. The brain injury work started as group sessions and was coordinated with a fellow student studying speech therapy. We enjoyed working together. He appreciated me sharing my experiences with speech impediment associated with seizures and brain surgery. He taught me how a speech therapist would have worked with me had I pursued the assistance. The work with people suffering with brain injury was fascinating for me as we learned to work together as a counselor and therapist. Although there were many people interested in participating, the program was cancelled due to transportation issues for those needing care.

Mobility has been the greatest challenge for most people dealing with epilepsy because they often have minimal transportation, often due to their driver license being suspended or terminated, making it difficult to obtain mental health support. In most cases, when a person has a seizure, the state will suspend their driver's license from thirty days to one year. Dealing with the diagnosis of epilepsy is traumatic, the isolation that often goes with it makes the situation even worse.

Most of my clients had comorbid conditions because they struggled with depression and anxiety, which they treated with illegal drugs or alcohol. In many cases, they were addicted to both. Some were dealing with high anxiety, caused by seizures or abuse, which they attempted to treat through alcoholism. I had several clients who suffered with bipolar disorder, who self-treated with heroin. I found a commonality with many of them, especially those with bipolar disorders. There are similarities in what happens during my seizures and what they experience in their manic, and especially depressive, episodes. A manic episode was comparable to a seizure as once you recovered from it, I felt so good and fortunate enough to be alive. Depression would result from my speech impediments and the inability to totally function for several days after a seizure. Taking higher doses of an ASD would also cause a change in my brain chemistry leading to depression or becoming very angry about minor issues.

I shared very little about myself with them, however my ability to relate with their depression and anxiety gave me a perspective that enabled me to quickly build trusting relationships. For many of them, it was the first time they talked to someone who could relate to what they were dealing with in their lives. The therapy centered on the cause and events that triggered the addictive behavior. Until the client understood the cause, they had no reason to stay clean. They were motivated through a spiritual connection with God to find meaning in their lives and develop a faith to replace their addictive behavior.

There was a client in his mid-twenties who was dealing with bipolar disorder. He told me about another therapist he had seen and how the counselor could not relate to his problem. He then thanked me for working with him because I shared some of my experiences with seizures that he could correlate to his bipolar disorder. He had never understood what his bipolar disorder was, but he had seen it in his father and was now dealing with it himself. The therapy focused on helping him realize why he acted and felt the way he did and how to discover meaning to what was happening. The major part of therapy came through building a spiritual relationship with God. At the end of the first six months, I had to leave because class was over and would not be able to keep in touch with him. He left the mission a few days later and started using heroin again in disorder to stabilize his disorder.

I did my next round of clinicals at a separate agency and then returned to the mission four months after my previous clinical work there had ended. Within two weeks, the same client was accepted back into the mission. We saw each other in the hallway, and we both felt a spiritual calling to work together again. I would be his counselor for four more months and had him work on seeking medical assistance from a psychologist.

Soon after starting our clinical sessions again, he told me his favorite scripture reading was from Matthew 19:25: "With God all things are possible." He now understood why his mood had changed so drastically in such a short period of time. He no longer felt any guilt about who he was as he understood his mood was due to his bipolar disorder caused by brain chemistry. Unfortunately, obtaining appropriate care for bipolar disorder may be difficult for those with little resources or income.

HOPE Instilled

My clients suffering from brain injury were the most challenging for me, as I had moments of reflection of my own experience. Often, we inspired one another, for the clients searched for positive reinforcement and someone to help process his/her life events. I was blessed with an opportunity to apply everything I learned through my life journey and the refinement as an intern in the pastoral counseling program.

At the end of my fourth year, I met a peer who was dealing with seizures and recovery from brain surgery. She had a section of her left temporal lobe removed and was spiritually inspired to become a counselor. A good part of her concerns was on having the self-confidence needed to be able to complete the program. She shared with me how her concerns were resolved when she learned about my ability to complete the courses and desire to progress. I never realized the influence my story was having on people. Although we got to see each other only for a moment, she helped me discover a new meaning in my journey. She graduated six months after me. Hope inspired now in two ways: one through the definition of the word itself and another in the acronyms. The definition I have for *hope* is this: "There is meaning in what is happening, learn, build, believe, for life can be better." The acronym, through the Epilepsy Foundation, was "Helping Other People with Epilepsy." Through my own studies and experience, I made my own revision to be "Helping Other People Everywhere."

Chapter 16
The National Counseling Exam

Do your best

It was the spring semester of my fifth and final year, and I had completed nineteen of the twenty-two courses, including all my clinical work required to graduate. If everything went as planned, my last class would be completed in the summer semester. The biggest challenge now was the National Counseling Exam, known as the NCE. The NCE is required in most states to obtain clinical licensing and is often taken as a student has completed or only has a few classes left to complete in a counseling program. There were several study guides and a program on CDs used to prepare for the exam. For five months, I listened to the CDs repeatedly and read the study guide several times. It was not unusual for me to miss the same question repeatedly. Due to work and classes, my brain was working hard, and I was stressed. Finding time to effectively study for the exam was difficult because it was not worth studying or listening to the CDs when I was tired because the memory of what was heard or read was shut down.

When the day came to take the exam, I was apprehensive and had to calm down because being nervous made my brain want to follow the old paths—the dead ends to my memory. The exam was difficult, and each question consisted of several examples presented in the study guides I used. As I read the first twelve problems, I could not comprehend the subject matter. My brain turned blank, and my anxiety level shot through the roof. By taking a deep breath and relaxing for a minute, my attitude changed from "I must pass" to "Let's learn from this exam and take it again someday." The anxiety abated, and the new paths I had developed over the past few years reopened in my mind. Suddenly, I knew the answer to the next question and the next and the next.

The physical and mental exhaustion came after I completed the last problem. There was ten minutes left before having to turn the exam in, so I thumbed through the answer sheet, checking for problems I hadn't answered. I missed several questions due to my nervousness and associated loss of memory. Suddenly, I could find the file in my brain that covered the subject matter associated with most of those questions. I turned my answer sheet in after three hours and fifty-nine minutes, with one minute to spare! There were many people still working on the exam when I left the room. Now the only unanswered question left was "Did I pass?" Seems several of my associates had the same question. Overall, I was happy and amazed—happy the exam was over and amazed at making it this far to be able to take it. Miracles can and do happen.

It was several months before the results of the exam would come in the mail. The envelope was thin and contained only one page. In my engineering days, when a one-pager was received for the Professional Engineer exam, it meant you failed. I skipped the details and just went to the bottom to see my score. It was lower than I hoped and thought to myself, *you did your best.* Then I read the details, and there in small capital letters, saw PASSING. Not long before I thought that this would have been impossible for me. It was a reminder that through a strong spiritual faith, "all things are possible!"

Chapter 17

Self-Thesis

The Storm before the Calm

We often do not appreciate how good life is until after we live through a major life challenge, surrounded by self-doubt. Persevering through such times builds faith and hope for the future

I was getting more and more excited as I completed my fourth year of studies with only three courses to finish. One of the courses was Family Therapy, taught by Professor Richardson,[*] who guided me through my very first course and with his experience and faith inspired me to complete the program and become an effective pastoral counselor. When he asked me if I needed any special assistance taking the exams in the class, I smiled and said no. Four years of intense studies and working full-time as an engineer enabled my brain to develop new pathways (rewired) to access the memory. In order to accomplish my degree, I had to control my emotions and practiced the methods to remember the criteria repeatedly. I had to stay calm, not get stressed, and learn to patiently wait for the words to appear in my mind. I no longer needed special assistance when taking an exam, including additional time.

Professor Richardson inspired me to apply my experiences in relating to people with disabilities. He shared, "I was facilitated by what was already within you, which was a 'can-do' spirit and a motivation not to give up. I saw that in my mother as well. She did not let her epilepsy slow her down. She persevered and had an amazing, resilient spirit. So, witnessing her life, I was ready to encourage you to reach for greater heights when you and I were introduced the first time."

The last course I needed to complete was the professional seminar that focused on writing a pastoral reflection paper based on my journey to become a pastoral counselor. What better title could I have chosen then— "Sailing the Course: Meaning in the Storms." The paper focused on the pilgrimage of my living with epilepsy and recovery from surgery, then applying what was learned about myself to develop a professional ability to help other people.

Storms were a metaphor that demonstrated how life could be wearisome and still build character; they can make a person strong or break them. I used sailing as a lens through which to view life events, survival, recovery, and a spiritual calling. The analogy is that of an experienced sailor who has felt a spiritual closeness when under sail. The sailor faces challenges, including the inability to see or control the wind, which is vital to the operation of the boat. Just as rough waters and high winds impact a sailor's ability to sail, serious life events and tragedy influence a person's strength to find meaning in life, faith, and still have hope for the future.

---

[*] Professor Richardson taught my first course (humanities) and one of the last (family therapy).

I was writing about my future with exposure to people dealing with trauma, addictions, and physical and/or brain injuries. The goal was to instill hope and confidence in others as they face the storms they encounter in life. Even before completing the paper, another very serious storm arrived.

My brother-in-law, Michael, was in the hospital for open-heart surgery. The surgery was successful, and he was progressing well until there was confusion regarding his treatment among the staff. Michael had been suffering for over fifteen years with a degenerative spinal condition and required pain medication. Some of the staff were not made aware of this and refused, based on experience with people addicted to pain medications, to provide the appropriate medication. His pain became excruciating, and over the next five days, he suffered three more heart attacks. After the second heart attack, he had met with one of the pastoral staff and found peace within himself to accept whatever would happen and secured his relationship with God. Two days later, he had his third heart attack, slipped into a coma, and was kept alive in a comatose state by lowering his body temperature in hopes that he would recover.

For the next three days, I was with my sister Susan and Michael's family while we waited to see if he would recover. There were late nights where Susan agonized over making tough decisions and suffered the trauma of having watched the man she loved suffer with severe pain, then resuscitated after his heart stopped time and again, and was now possibly brain dead. What we did not realize was Michael may have had some cognitive awareness each time his heart stopped and as the doctor's worked to revive him. Michael suffered with seeing death over and over.

When visiting Michael in intensive care, I could see the lines of the EEG and knew he was dead, kept alive only by machine, but did not want to share this with anyone. I did well as a brother, friend, and counselor for the family, yet when alone, I broke down several times as I lost the brother I loved. After three days, the doctors attempted to revive Michael by raising his body temperature. As it slowly increased, his body started to tremble and slipped into a grand mal seizure. To stop the seizure, they quickly lowered his body temperature, and he was pronounced dead by the medical staff. My sister Susan and Michael's family were devastated as we all watched the hospital staff do their work. The pastoral care unit was outstanding. We watched him slip into death as the support systems were turned off. Susan had wept little because she was already so traumatized by what happened that week. The tears would come later. I did not have time to dwell on what had just happened. There would be an opportunity for that later. To keep myself together emotionally, I focused on completing the paper and graduating.

Through Michael, came the traumatic loss of a loved one. This was expressed in the reflection paper, and how my faith grew during this time by relying on God. The is the same faith that brought me through such trying times and made me spiritually stronger with each challenging event in my life, living through such trials as epilepsy, brain surgery, recovery, and again a loved one's death.

In my paper I described how in my studies and work as a counselor intern, I could exercise my abilities to relate to clients and help to instill in them hope and faith through their persevering through their own storms in life. To overcome what they believed to be impossible, they had developed a new perspective of themselves and focused on a life being filled with greater meaning by having a faith in God.

The staff reviewed my paper, and I received a passing grade (it was pass/fail). I was amazed at how quickly five years had gone by and the person I had become. There were moments when doubt nearly brought everything to a halt, but hope brought me through. Perseverance made me a new man.

The next step in practicing counseling was taking the state exam. The documentation and paperwork seemed to take forever. Then the day came to take the exam. This was much easier than the NCE, and it went very well. Within a few days, the letter was received the much-awaited letter from the state certification board; I was now a licensed graduate professional counselor (LGPC).

Section 7
New Beginnings

Chapter 18
The Engineer Retires

Retirement from a career does not mean the end to working; it is a new beginning to apply what you learn in life. Share your experience; you may bring hope to others

My final couple of years with the Army Corps of Engineers involved sharing my knowledge through developing training programs. These programs were unique because of my experience in the roles needed to complete a project—the planner, designer, contracting officer, and construction representative. Management thought it good to have these presented to the staff so they could understand the efforts required by each part of the organization and the decision-making process in completing a project.

I kept quiet about turning in my paperwork for retirement, then a young man who had worked with me for several years joked to the staff we worked with, "It's okay for you to retire now, because I'm not learning anything new from you anymore." He had become my right hand in helping with the training programs and was now doing some of the presentations. In fact, he was ahead of me on formatting and resourcing presentations. That's when I told everyone the paperwork required for retirement was being processed. He apologized, thinking he had been part of the cause of my leaving, but was assured he was more than capable of handling some of my responsibilities and it was just time for me to leave. My retirement became official in the early fall.

Chapter 19
Epilepsy Advocacy

Advocacy is the ability to step forward and share personal experience and influence the perspective of a life situation for others

It was time to relax and take some time off. My brain and body needed some rest after five years of working full time and studying many hours each week. Retirement from the Army Corps and completing the curriculum at Loyola University left me with no work or school responsibilities. My pastoral counseling clinical work would start in January and in the meantime, there was still some work to do as a mentor with the Chesapeake Chapter of the Epilepsy Foundation.* My free time would start to diminish as a series of opportunities came along.

Through the Chesapeake Chapter came a recommendation to be trained in the UPLIFT program, developed by Emory University and funded through the Center for Disease Control and Prevention. (UPLIFT stands for Using Practice and Learning to Increase Favorable Thoughts.) This was a ten-week program starting in October focusing on helping groups of people diagnosed with epilepsy to manage stress. With completion, came the certification to facilitate groups of people, help them learn they are not alone in dealing with seizures, and develop skills to reduce stress in their lives.

My work with the Epilepsy Foundation led to a call from the Department of Defense, and their Peer Review Medical Research Program (PRMRP). Handling epilepsy had been made part of the program due to the number of soldiers who came home after surviving head injuries that developed into seizure disorders. After the interview with the staff, I was asked to become a consumer peer reviewer. They were excited about my joining the program and asked me to be a speaker at the kick-off dinner to share my own experience and the importance of the program. There would be many different professional review teams of various backgrounds. Several peers with disabilities shared their personal experiences too, enabling me to understand the significance of the work about to take place.

I was unsure what it would be like talking to a group of people that consisted of doctors and researchers from all over the United States. If this was happening nine years earlier, I would have been visibly shaking with anxiety and would not have been capable of participating. My exposure to talking to and leading groups through work and classes, enabled my brain to rewire and build confidence.

The review board for the consumer advocacy was held in a hotel. As I walked across the parking lot to enter the building, my anxiety level increased. Despite this, another part of me was fascinated and interested in everything that was happening around me. Many rooms were set up for various meetings. There were advocates and professionals from all around the country. Some

---

* It has since become the Maryland Chapter of the Epilepsy Foundation

of the most interesting people were like me—the consumer advocates. Once there, I was handed the key to my room and my name tag for identification; everything was very well organized.

I needed to get to my room and drop off my bag of clothes for the three days of the review boards. As the doors to the elevator opened, I was overwhelmed with a strong smell of a cleaning fluid. It smelled just like the cleaner at Johns Hopkins Hospital, when I had my extended EEG. The hallway seemed just like Johns Hopkins, it was bright, and the walls were white. The doors to the rooms looked just like the doors to the recovery rooms. It was then I realized this was a flashback of looking down the hallway at the Johns Hopkins Hospital and smelling the disinfectant. An aura came on strong and my heartbeat increased rapidly.

Instead of succumbing to a panic attack, as typical in the past, I allowed myself to become fascinated by what was happening. My studies in becoming a counselor, led to my performing a self-analysis and evaluating the trigger to the fear and panic I was about to experience. It was a session of countertransference within me. My self-analysis kept my brain focused on the reality of the present and I gained control over the feelings of panic. My heartbeat returned to normal, and the aura stopped. The hallway was no longer like the one in the hospital. It was moderately lit with wood-finish paneling and a dark-colored carpet. I felt tired, went into my room, and lay down to rest and be prepared for the evening events.

Everyone who was involved in a research review board was at the dinner and was seated with the people they were to work with. Each team consisted of doctors and scientist from the most prestigious and renown universities, hospitals, and research centers in the country. The room was filled with teams similar to mine, some doing research on various diseases and recovery for the wounded soldiers.

As we finished eating, the speakers were called up to the front of the room. When it was my turn, I walked up to the podium and looked over the people sitting at their tables. I was nervous and reminded myself of the importance of staying calm. Reading the script that I wrote went well until I come to the part about my surgery. My mind started to fill with fear as I thought about what had happened, and of where I was now. I lost my ability to concentrate and my brain shut down for a moment. By taking a deep breath, holding it, and slowly letting it out I was able to gain the control needed to continue. I now felt in control of the dark emotions of panic and fear, bringing about a calmness that made me smile. My reading skills returned, and I completed the speech.

Everyone was moved by what they heard. When I got back to my table, the chief of the Epilepsy Review Board stood up and shook my hand and thanked me for speaking. He then went and got me dessert and something to drink. He noticed that I was having a little difficulty responding. It was not because I was having a seizure—it was due to struggling with my emotions while fighting back tears. This was a place I never even dreamed of in helping other people; it was another step forward in my recovery.

Through my counseling studies, I learned that it was common for someone with my challenges to become immobile or depressed when faced with daunting tasks like public speaking. Repeated exposure to challenging situations can help one gain control over their emotions. What helped me was taking on the role of a counselor and conducting an evaluation of myself. This experience enabled me to learn to control the uncontrollable within oneself.[*] At that time I smiled and thanked the Lord for the opportunity to not just learn but to also understand how the mind works and our ability to reprogram our brains. The engineer in me kept working to determine the cause of such sensations. Sometimes there was no racing heartbeat, only the sensation of an aura and anxiety triggered by seeing something that was similar to what I saw when experiencing a seizure in the past. This would remind me of what a seizure was like and the outcome. When I get that the aura is not strong, it may simply have been triggered by the memory of a dark time in my life.

My work as a licensed graduate professional counselor (LGPC) and coordinator started at the Westminster Rescue Mission a few weeks earlier than planned. I was bored with my time off and quite frankly was excited to begin my work as a clinician. The staff was a tremendous help in assisting me with my work and family life. My clinical work required being ready and willing to lead a group of men in a chapel as they found ways to overcome their addictions. Individual work was on a continuous basis. Helping men through the detoxification stage—from heroin and other drugs—required my being available and willing to listen to them. Motivation came as clients learned to be open with one another. Having a spiritual bond with God and understanding their role in life was essential in being effective. Through this experience, I learned the importance of counselor self-care to prevent burnout. I had to continually remind myself that my role was that of the messenger and listener, and not taking on the responsibilities of the client; understanding this was crucial.

Nine years after my surgery, I was accepted into a training program at a hospital that prepares pastors in visiting patients. On the first day, we were given a tour of the hospital. I was nervous and I wondered if I was ready. Walking through the OBGYN section reminded me of the times my children were born and brought fond memories. As we walked through the emergency care center, we saw many people needing care. The beds and equipment reminded me of my own visits, and I started to become anxious. At the end of the day, I asked the instructor if we could visit the emergency room again., thinking more exposure was helpful in my own recovery and getting control of the anxiety.

As we approached one end of the emergency care center, we came across a family with an elderly parent who was dying. I was able to watch the instructor in action and rendered aid. The instructor seemed like a natural, and I felt that someday it would be my role as well—just not yet. The memories of what I experienced at Johns Hopkins were still to vivid.

---

[*] This is one manner of obtaining control of posttraumatic stress disorder. A condition often overlooked with people dealing with chronic traumatic situations, such as seizures.

Chapter 20
New Relationships

Knowing that there is a way it can be done is most effective in having the ability to overcome life challenges. This is when hope is implanted in you; little do you realize the day will come when someone else is struggling to climb the mountain of a life challenge and looks up and sees you. It is a way of instilling hope in others

A relationship with someone dealing with seizures must be based on a love for the person, not a love for their possessions and not a love that exists just during the good times. True love is revealed in what you do when the times get tough. Relationships can build then become closer and stronger during challenging times and can be enhanced through the perspectives of the individuals and family involved.

Unfortunately, the effect of serious health issues can often lead to the end of a relationship. My relationship with Becky began to dissolve as my seizures slowly progressed and became intractable. Furthermore, my disability to remember names and my brain shutting down when I was tired was frustrating not only to me, but to her too. This left me feeling more alone in a battle that was driving us further apart. Home no longer became the place I wanted to be—I had too many memories there of the hard times I had with my seizures, the surgery, and recovery and the impact it all had on Becky.

With the pressure mounting because of my counseling work and dealing with home life, it was time for the two of us to separate. I moved out of the house, into an apartment, and into a new beginning. Eventually, I moved from the hectic fast-paced Baltimore/Washington area to the tranquil farm country of North Carolina, where some of my family lived. It was quite a change. I continued to work with the Epilepsy Foundation in Maryland while assisting some of the agencies in North Carolina. I felt more at ease with the hassles of the metropolitan areas behind me.

Little did I know there was a half-marathon held there in support of people with epilepsy, and I would become a close friend and caregiver of my next-door neighbor who remarkably recovered from a stroke, then started having seizures.

Chapter 21
Caregiving

The fundamentals of caregiving are listening, caring, asking, thanking, sharing, and learning

The Role of the Mentor

A mentor is someone with real-life experiences who can help other people who are dealing with similar issues. As a mentor with the Epilepsy Foundation, I met many people diagnosed with epilepsy. Over time I also met their caregivers—typically the parents and spouses. With every caregiver I met there was a learning curve for me as each person was different in their knowledge of seizures, their relationship with the individual they cared for, and the control of their own emotions and feelings. Many of them were overwhelmed by their fears and ignorance of seizures, especially those who were caring for someone recently diagnosed. The doctors provided excellent information concerning the medical treatment and resources; however, they were unequipped to provide enough mental and emotional support.

Soon after volunteering, I received a call from a woman recently diagnosed with epilepsy. She was worried about how her two young children would react when she had a grand mal seizure. Her husband's shift work increased the time she would be alone with her children, and she wanted them to be prepared. The very young children suddenly had the responsibility of an adult.

During our training session, we talked about rendering first aid and the responsibilities of the child caregiver. When I had her pretend to have a seizure, the younger child, the eight-year-old, stayed with me as the older ten-year-old ran out of the room, screaming and was close to a state of panic. She did grab the phone on her way out and called their father. When she returned to the room, she was sobbing, with tears streaming down her face as she feared her mother would die from a seizure.

Children can be strong when necessary. However, it was difficult to determine how they would react in such a situation. They first must understand what was happening to their parent or sibling, know who to contact for help, and the address of where they live. Having access to a cell phone and knowing how to make the emergency call was very important. Cell phones today can give the position of the call to the EMS personnel, so we had to make sure the GPS setting was activated.

Most importantly, caregivers, especially children, also need attention when the seizure is over. They need to understand what had happened, and that they could do nothing to control it. They may feel guilt, so it is important that they realize that it is not their fault. It is amazing what young children conceive from a situation. Even my oldest son, at the age of two, recognized something was wrong with me and that I needed help at times. When he was a teenager, he had an uncanny ability to stay calm, contact emergency services, and know where to obtain the information the paramedics would need. His greatest fear was similar to the girl mentioned earlier—watching a loved one die from a seizure.

Education provided by people with experience is very effective in maintaining the proper perspective of epilepsy. Ignorance feeds fear in everyone and leads to people to isolate an individual who has seizures. Isolation and fear lead to depression and a loss of hope. Mentors need to step forward and volunteer to help their peers and caregivers. Although having earned a degree and license in counseling, being a mentor came first.

Role of the Counselor

As a counselor working with the Maryland Chapter of the Epilepsy Foundation, I focused on helping those diagnosed with epilepsy. This was later expanded to include the caregivers when I started working with Melanie whose daughter, Grace, for some unknown reason, had forty-four seizures in fifty-two days. While Grace was having seizures, Melanie would go for days without sleep and only slept a few hours when she did. Melanie's capability to function as a mother to Grace and her twin brother was impaired by her fears and love for her children.

For Grace, the doctors devised a treatment plan, involving some of the latest medications, to bring her seizures under control. However, the side effects of the medications changed her personality. Initially, her medication caused her to slow down and dampened her ability to perform in class. She was no longer the energetic little girl who was a whiz at math and reading. Her bright smile had faded, and she just merely functioned. She would eat little, was no longer able to learn anything, and suffered with depression. Her reading ability, which was outstanding for a child her age, diminished. And she could no longer remember her last name. Nothing could excite her, except for the fear of having another seizure. She was no longer the little four-year-old who loved to read and play.

Over time, the doctors worked to find the most effective medication that would control Grace's seizures with minimal impact to her personality. Changing her medication and finding the appropriate dosage helped her regain some of her memory and enabled her to participate with other children. Over the next several months, it was difficult to determine if she was having absence seizures, a reaction to her medication, or was just bored with class. Eventually, Grace came to one of our monthly group sessions. I struggled with my emotions as I talked with this beautiful little five-year-old girl. For her mother to watch her have so many seizures in such a short time must have felt like having your soul torn away.

After eighteen months of treatment, Grace was taken off her medication because her EEG no longer indicated any seizure activity. She could laugh again! Her competency to learn increased significantly as her brain was no longer affected by medication.

Melanie appreciated the application of my insight to seizures with the sessions we had. Many of the sessions had to be held over the phone due to accessibility issues and time restraints. By applying my own experience and educating Melanie about epilepsy I was able to help her understand what to do, and what to ask and sometimes demand of her neurologist. Based on what was told to her she would often respond with, "You need to share this." Melanie and Grace motivated me to develop a five-week counseling program for caregivers.

The Role of the Caregiver

The caregiver program included training in first aid for the person with seizures and the caregiver, education about seizures and treatment, the perspective of the person with epilepsy, maintaining healthy relationships, and taking on challenges in a healthy manner. It was continually revised with each group because the more people shared the more was learned about the caregiver's perspective. One of the most effective parts of the program was the ability of everyone to share their experiences and learn from each other. Knowing they were not alone and sharing with each other the stress of a caregiver's situation seemed very a very effective treatment for them. Little did I know that one day my role would expand to becoming the caregiver of someone who lived close to me.

To lessen the stressors related to my work, and living near Washington, DC, I moved to a small town near the water in North Carolina. I did not know anyone, yet the people in the neighborhood were friendly, and I began to meet people throughout the community. I never expected to meet people with whom I had so much in common—Sara and James.

I like to run and was looking for a group to join. While researching races in the area, I was amazed to see a half marathon and 5K race held every February in Washington, North Carolina. The person in charge of the program was James, who had seizures as a child which eventually became intractable. When he was seventeen, he had a lobectomy to regain control, and the surgery was very effective. Because he loved to run, he developed the *Race for Epilepsy Half Marathon/5K*, the only half-marathon in the country to support people with epilepsy. We had dinner together and surprised each other by how our experience with seizures and surgery were very similar.

Two weeks after moving into my new home, Sara moved into the house next door. She was new to the area and only knew a few people through her work. The day she moved in, I was working in my yard and saw her approaching me. As we chatted, we learned how much we had in common—sailing, fishing, and a second career in a ministry field. We both had suffered brain injuries; she had a stroke six months before. She had recovered well; however, the stroke left her with an affected sense of touch in her left arm and leg. After learning a little more about my experience with living with epilepsy she felt more comfortable in sharing more of her story in surviving a hemorrhagic stroke. She explained how she sometimes struggles with organizing thoughts and writing sentences—many similarities to my recovering from surgery. I was witnessing a miracle standing in front of me as the doctors never thought Sara would survive her stroke, let alone be able to relocate and continue to work at her career.

One evening, I heard the doorbell ring, and Sara was standing near the doorway. She apologized for interrupting me and said she needed help. When she came into the house, she asked me to look at her eyes. Her eyes were moving independently of each other even though she was trying to look straight at me. She said she saw her dog run down the hallway in her house numerous times. In actuality, the dog had gone down the hallway one time. Her brain just kept playing it repeatedly. I was surprised she could still see and was capable enough to walk to my house. She was having a seizure, and I hurriedly drove her to the hospital. Later that evening, they transported her to another hospital with a neurological care facility and performed a twenty-four-hour EEG.

The challenge to both of us was her seizures as they became more intense and occurring more often. There were times she called or texted me with "I'm having a seizure!" Within a few months her seizures spread to other sections of her brain and became more acute, with her body contracting and half her face distorting. Throughout this, she could still hear what was happening around her. She told me, "I feel safe when I hear your voice," because she knew I could take care of her.

Although I had seen many people have seizures, this was different. Seeing a friend have multiple partial and complex seizures, brought to me a better understanding of the emotional toll they can have on a caregiver. In some ways, caring for her was easier because of my ability to relate to what was happening to her. In other ways, it was very difficult because of having lived through the trauma of the seizures. In just over a year, the seizures would spread throughout her brain affecting most of her body. Witnessing her have an extended grand mal seizure helped me truly understand what my family and friends had lived through. Fortunately, the work with Melanie brought some techniques I could use to cope with the stress through the caregiver program. I had to define my emotional and physical limits, but with only a few people in the town who could help Sara and my proximity to her, I was the one often called on and reached the stage of burnout.

Even with several neurologist on our side trying to find a treatment for the seizures, obtaining any control was not possible without substantial side effects from the AEDs. For me, to be most the most effective caregiver required taking care of myself. However, the situation continued to decline and became more intense as the seizures spread to other areas of the brain and lasted longer and longer. They were occurring more often, leading me to experience a burnout that went as far as triggering simple partial seizures in me and reliving my own experiences. Eventually, she could no longer continue to work or live by herself and moved out of the area. It was another lesson on how we couldn't control everything that happens around us, and the impact such trauma may have.

The two of us had talked about our life experiences and were aware that the most effective treatment in recovery from any situation is having a positive outlook and moving forward. It was hard to move forward for a while after Sara moved away because of the memory of the dark times in my life returning to me. Having already known how far a positive outlook can bring a person to healing assured me that having hope was the key to recovery. What happened with Sara was another lesson on loss. Persevering through such an experience was not easy, but time and faith made it possible to recover from it.

Sometimes the plans we hope for are not what the Lord has planned.

Epilogue

Seizures are a reminder about how fragile life is, and that life should be cherished.

Although I have written much about what it is like to live with epilepsy, it should be noted that it is only a part of my life, not all my life. I have been able to live a full and prosperous life because I searched for meaning and refused defeat. This is the engineer in me, who is always searching for solutions when facing challenges, and the counselor, who focuses on the positive. I like to smile and laugh, even when life is challenging and seems out of control.

I am no longer the nineteen-year-old who was warned by his father to keep quiet about my disability, because my disability became an ability I am blessed with. It enabled me to help people whose experiences with seizures overwhelmed them. Seizures are reminders of how fragile life is and that life should be cherished.

The writing of this book began when I was told in my counseling courses that I should share my story. It required me to relive some of the darkest times in my life and when I faced those deep feelings of frustration, anger, defeat, and brokenness. Yet, with each event I wrote about, I felt stronger because those times helped me appreciate what I have been training for as someone that could inspire hope.

What carried me through my dark times was a faith that God has a plan for all of us. It was nurtured through the hope that there was meaning to what was happening. Seizures taught me that being a good leader requires relying on other people, being humble, and seeking the good in any situation. Experience makes us stronger and able to help one another. As a counselor, I often wonder what my client is in training for, as they share their challenging experiences.

My hope for those of you who are dealing with seizures is that you receive the help needed to control them. That there is a caregiver who is ready when needed and loves you for who you are. That you overcome the fear of a seizure and they become only a temporary setback. May you still be able to laugh and feel joy. The day may come when someone will look at you and be inspired by your experience and ability to live with a disability. When that happens, you become a source and beacon of hope.

Appendix A
Basic Guide for Caregivers

1. Don't panic! It shuts down your brain's ability to reason and respond appropriately.
2. Be aware that the individual in need may be able to see and/or hear what is happening.
3. Protect the head with a cushion, pillow, or soft object; your hands work well too.
4. Talk to the person throughout the stages of their seizure or stroke in a calm voice to reflect you care and are with them. Use simple statements such as "You're safe. I am with you."
5. Set up a support system, especially if you cannot lift the person. This can be a neighbor or a close friend.
6. Keep a list of the medications, including dosage and time of day they are administered. Have a copy available to give to emergency personnel and those providing medical assistance or treatment.
7. Find people you can talk to about what you are experiencing. You may find groups near you or on Facebook. You may also contact your local chapter of the Epilepsy Foundation to obtain training and other information.
8. Be sure to take care of yourself. Take time to do what you like to do, especially in relieving stress.
9. Seek help through family or friends. You can only be a good caregiver if you are healthy.
10. Obtain professional counseling to help manage the stress of being a caregiver.
11. Seek emergency support when the following occur:
    a. If the seizure last longer than five minutes (ictal state) than usual or the person has difficulty breathing
    b. If the person has recurring seizures in a short period of time
    c. If the seizure causes injury to the body or head
    d. If you need support; a seizure can be harder on you than the person having it
12. Be prepared to give first aid through education to those who witness the seizure.

An Epileptic's Perspective

The following is based on what was needed to pull people through. Negativity drives depression; find a way to be positive. Here are some key points to consider as a family member:

1. When I have a seizure, please be *aware* I may be able to see and hear what you do and say. Try to be *positive*.
2. Speak calmly. Tell me you *care*.
3. Make this *our* battle, not my battle.
4. Be a part of my life, not a *critic* of my life.
5. Inspire me for what I have achieved despite my disability. *Laugh* with me.
6. Help me set high levels of recovery through setting *realistic* milestones. Then *cheer* me on.
7. All the other parts of the body when injured may take a few days to several weeks to heal. The brain requires more time, sometimes years and a desire to do so. *Be patient*
8. Hiding feelings leads to separation, it's okay to *cry with me*.
9. Hold me occasionally. *Being touched instills importance.*
10. Most importantly, *love me for who I am.*

Appendix B
Epilepsy Support Agencies

Epilepsy Foundation
8301 Professional Place East, Suite 200
Landover, Maryland: 20785-2353
Phone: 301-459-3700
24/7 Epilepsy and Seizures Helpline: 1-800-332-1000
Spanish Speakers Only: 1-866-748-8008
Email: ContactUs@efa.org

Epilepsy Foundation, Maryland Chapter
Mary Wontrop, executive director: mwontrop@efa.org
5349 Glen Arm Road
Glen Arm, MD 21057
Phone: (301) 918-3789

Citizens United for Research in Epilepsy (CURE)
430 W. Erie, Suite 210
Chicago, IL, 60654
(312) 255-1801
1 (844) 231-2873 (toll-free)

Triangle North Carolina Epilepsy
Raleigh-Durham-Chapel Hill
References multiple support agencies in North Carolina
www.trianglencepilepsy.com

Project UPLIFT
http://managingepilepsywell.org/programs/uplift.html.
If they want to know if there is someone trained to deliver Project UPLIFT in their state, there is
a list of trained providers by state at the bottom of the page here:
http://managingepilepsywell.org/programs/uplift_training.html

Appendix C
Types of Seizures

Some types of seizures include the following[*]:

Generalized seizures. Generalized seizures involve both sides of the brain. There is loss of consciousness and a postictal state after the seizure occurs. Types of generalized seizures include the following:

Absence seizures (also called petit mal seizures). These seizures are characterized by a brief altered state of consciousness and staring episodes. Typically, the person's posture is maintained during the seizure. The mouth or face may twitch, or the eyes may blink rapidly. The seizure usually lasts no longer than thirty seconds. When the seizure is over, the person may not recall what just occurred and may go on with his or her activities, acting as though nothing happened. These seizures may occur several times a day. This type of seizure is sometimes mistaken for a learning problem or behavioral problem. Absence seizures almost always start between ages four to twelve years.[†]

Atonic (also called drop attacks). With atonic seizures, there is a sudden loss of muscle tone, and the person may fall from a standing position or suddenly drop his or her head. During the seizure, the person is limp and unresponsive.

Generalized tonic-clonic seizures (GTC, or also called grand mal seizures). The classic form of this kind of seizure, which may not occur in every case, is characterized by five distinct phases. The body, arms, and legs will flex (contract), extend (straighten out), and tremor (shake), followed by a clonic period (contraction and relaxation of the muscles) and the postictal period. Not all these phases may be seen in everyone with this type of seizure. During the postictal period, the person may be sleepy, have problems with vision or speech, and may have a bad headache, fatigue, or body aches.[‡]

Myoclonic seizures. This type of seizure refers to quick movements or sudden jerking of a group of muscles. These seizures tend to occur in clusters, meaning they may occur several times a day or for several days in a row.

Infantile spasms. This rare type of seizure disorder occurs in infants before six months of age. There is a high occurrence rate of this seizure when the child is awakening or when he or she is trying to go to sleep. The infant usually has brief periods of

---

[*]From the Johns Hopkins Medicine Health Library under nervous system disorders, epilepsy, and seizures.

[†]Absence—the earlier childhood absences almost always remit by late childhood; the later childhood ones (e.g. age of onset six to eight) are called juvenile absences and usually continue and form tonic-clonic seizures in adulthood.

[‡]The bilateral tonic-clonic seizures are by far the most dangerous. They often cause brief postictal paralysis with impaired breathing. Those who have seizures out of sleep while facedown are at special risk for asphyxiation (SUDEP).

movement of the neck, trunk, or legs that lasts for a few seconds. Infants may have hundreds of these seizures a day. This can be a serious problem and can have long-term complications that affect growth and development.

Febrile seizures. This type of seizure is associated with fever and is not epilepsy, although a fever may trigger a seizure in a child who has epilepsy. These seizures are more commonly seen in children between six months and five years of age, and there may be a family history of this type of seizure. Febrile seizures that last less than fifteen minutes are called simple and typically do not have long-term neurological effects. Seizures lasting more than fifteen minutes are called complex, and there may be long-term neurological changes in the child.

Focal or partial seizures. Focal seizures take place when abnormal electrical brain function occurs in one or more areas of one side of the brain. Focal seizures may also be called partial seizures. With focal seizures, particularly with complex focal seizures, a person may experience an aura, or premonition, before the seizure occurs. The most common aura involves feelings, such as déjà vu, impending doom, fear, or euphoria. Visual changes, hearing abnormalities, or changes in the sense of smell can also be auras. Two types of focal seizures include the following:

Simple focal seizures. The person may have different symptoms depending on which area of the brain is involved. If the abnormal electrical brain function is in the occipital lobe (the back part of the brain that is involved with vision), sight may be altered, but muscles are more commonly affected. The seizure activity is limited to an isolated muscle group, such as the fingers, or to larger muscles in the arms and legs. Consciousness is not lost in this type of seizure. The person may also experience sweating, nausea, or may become pale.

Complex focal seizures. This type of seizure commonly occurs in the temporal lobe of the brain—the area of the brain that controls emotion and memory function. Consciousness is usually lost during these seizures. Losing consciousness may not mean that a person passes out—sometimes, a person stops being aware of what's going on around him or her. The person may look awake but may have a variety of unusual behaviors. These behaviors may range from gagging, lip-smacking, running, screaming, crying, or laughing. When the person regains consciousness, he or she may complain of being tired or sleepy after the seizure. This is called the postictal period.

Made in the USA
Columbia, SC
07 May 2020